Our Family Heritage

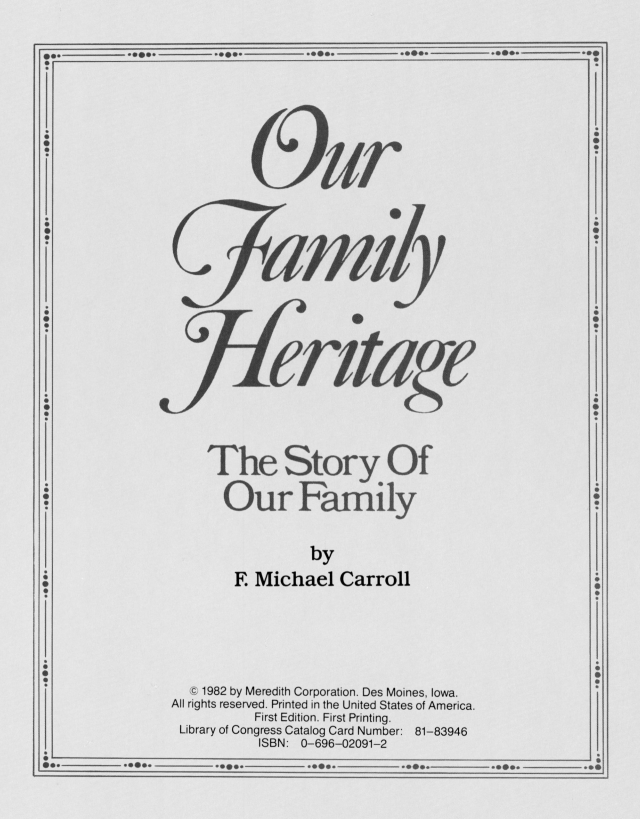

Our Family Heritage

The Story Of Our Family

by
F. Michael Carroll

Library of Congress Catalog Card Number: 81-83946
ISBN: 0-696-02091-2

The Story of Our Family is Unique in History

Philosophers agree that the most vital instant of your life is that critical "moment of truth" when you fully realize for the first time that you are a completely new and unique person in the history of mankind, that among all the billions of people since the beginning of time there has never been anyone exactly like you. Nor has there ever been anyone exactly like the countless men and women who were your ancestors.

Intellectually, emotionally and physically you are the one-of-a-kind product of the genes of the thousands of men and women from whom you have inherited an unbroken lineage as ancient as humanity itself. And like each of your forebears, you too will impress your own personal individuality upon the characteristics and potentials which you have inherited.

Consider the richness and variety of your family heritage. Among your ancestors and ancestresses were tribal chieftains, regal matriarchs, warriors, sailors, charlatans, beautiful courtesans, sturdy farmers, skillful artisans, poets, adventurers, saints and sinners. Whether they were humble or exalted, they had the courage and ingenuity to survive wars, pestilence, floods and famines—and for that you can be both proud and thankful.

When you explore the lives of your forefathers, you will discover instances of stubborn courage and daring, of decency and integrity, of high hopes and eccentricities, of self-sacrifice and enduring love. And you will see the same qualities reflected in the lives of the members of your family today.

As you write the stories of both of your families and ancestries in this handsome book, you will be permanently recording the life of each man and woman as an indispensable link in an unbroken chain which has existed for thousands of years. And as husband and wife, you will join together your two heritages into a new chain which will continue through your children in the generations to come.

Table of Contents

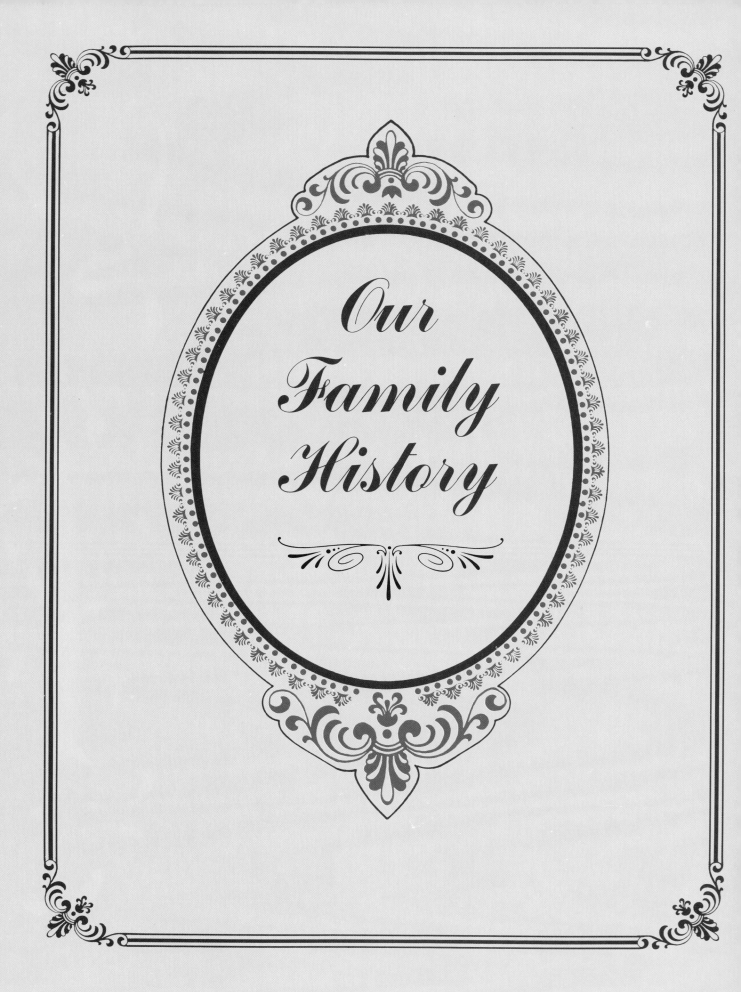

Our Family History

Writing the Story of Your Living Family and Your Ancestors

If you're genuinely interested in other people, and if you have a sense of pride in your family, you'll find that writing this book will be a hobby which is challenging, engrossing and truly worthwhile. As you gather the information for your Family Biographies and as you write the names in your Family Tree, you will sense the satisfaction of preserving the memories of the men and women you love and the ancestors to whom you owe so much.

Writing your Heritage Book will be a continuing source of satisfaction for you, and it will, of course, be enjoyed by all the members of your family. Probably its most meaningful achievement will be the heightened sense of personal identity and historic continuity which it will bring to your children and the generations of the future.

Sources of Information for Future Authors of This Heritage Book

You will be surprised at the varied sources of official records and helpful advice which are available to you. We have divided these sources into six categories:

1. **The members of your family.** Of course, you will interview or correspond with your relatives in order to gather the personal and factual information for their biographies. You will also want them to recall their memories of your ancestors and the other deceased members of your family. Of great importance will be the old family papers, records and memorabilia which they have stored away.

2. **Governmental agencies in this country.** There are many official record-keeping offices which will comply with your written requests for records of an ancestor's birth, marriage, death, immigration records, naturalization papers, military service, etc.

3. **The Genealogical Society of Utah.** This Society is affiliated with the Church of Jesus Christ of Latter Day Saints, usually called the Mormon Church. They have gathered and microfilmed the world's largest collection of genealogical records. These films can be viewed by people of all religious faiths in the Society's many Branch Libraries.

4. **Communities where your ancestors lived.** At the local level there are many sources of information about the lives of your ancestors: city halls, court houses, public libraries, genealogical societies, local historical societies, churches, cemeteries, schools, newspaper offices, etc.

5. **Sources of records in your ancestors' lands of origin.** Official archives, registry offices, churches and libraries in Europe will try to answer requests for copies of records pertaining to your an-

cestors if you supply them with adequate identification data.

6. ***Genealogical guides, research manuals and reference books.*** *In the following pages, we will refer to many helpful books which will help you in your study and research. In the Bibliography on page 23 are listed excellent guide books for beginners and for people seeking more advanced information.*

Before you begin writing in this Heritage Book, we suggest that you first purchase two lined notebooks (about 8¹/₂ by 11 inches), one for the family of the husband and one for the family of the wife. Assign one or two pages to each family member, relative and ancestor. As you collect information from the above sources, record it on the pages of the person or persons involved. After you have organized these notes, you can then write a concise and well-organized biography of the individual on the appropriate page in this book.

Writing Your First Biography

We suggest that you first write your own autobiography. It will then serve as a pattern to follow in gathering information for the biographies of the other members of your family.

Just sit down and start writing the story of your life in your notebook in a simple narrative style as if you were writing a letter to a close friend. You will be surprised how easily and quickly the memories will flow from your pen. For instance, "I was born July 9, 1940, in Davenport, Ohio. We lived in an old white framehouse at 2301 North Elm Street. My father, James William Smith, was an insurance salesman for the Connecticut Company. My mother, Jane Mason Smith, was a very lovely lady (and she still is) who was kept busy taking care of me and my sister Mary Ellen, two years older than me, and my brother James Junior, four years older. I can remember that my mother loved to garden and that we

had a lively black and white dog of mixed parentage named Bounce. I first attended Jefferson Elementary School, etc."

Don't be concerned with grammar or literary style. Just write about the memorable activities, events, people, places and dates of your life from your childhood to the present. You'll probably spend an evening or two outlining the story of your life. Before entering it in this book, arrange the material in proper sequence, eliminate or add thoughts, expand or shorten episodes. Write neatly for the benefit of future readers, and be sure to leave plenty of space for future entries.

The Importance of Old Family Papers and Memorabilia

Next, we recommend that you make a thorough search for any old family papers and memorabilia which you have stored away and perhaps forgotten. Wonderful ancestral information, both of human interest and factual value, can be obtained from old correspondence, newspaper clippings, family Bibles, diaries, books, business letters, birth and wedding announcements, invitations, death notices, obituaries, school report cards and yearbooks, photographs, snapshots, albums, ledgers, wills, leases, contracts, bills, checks, receipts and just about any papers or materials relating to your ancestors. In your future interviews with members of your family, be sure to ask them to collect all their old family nostalgia items and papers so that you can examine them.

*Store all of this material in a convenient box or drawer. As you read through it, you will find noteworthy references to events, people, places and dates about your relatives and ancestors which you can enter on the pages assigned to them in your notebooks. You will then be able to include the information in their individual biographies and in the appropriate chapters in the **Family Memories** section.*

Interviewing the Members of Your Family

When you explain the purpose of this Heritage Book to your relatives, you can be sure that they will appreciate your efforts to record the story of your family. Everyone is interested in their ancestors, and they will be happy to contribute their knowledge to you. Modesty may inhibit some of them from talking about themselves, but most of them will enjoy reminiscing about the important events and memories of their lives.

Your interviewing procedure can be simple and direct in the case of your own generation—your brothers and their wives, your sisters and their husbands and your cousins. During the interview, make pertinent notes in your notebook rather than trying to write a verbatim narrative which is tedious and time-wasting. Some people prefer to use a tape recorder.

First, ask them to begin with the dates and places of their births, and then let them tell you the stories of their lives with all the highlights and experiences which they consider noteworthy and which they would like to have remembered. If they have children, they will be happy to tell you everything you want to know about them.

Whether you interview relatives face-to-face, by telephone or letter, it is advisable to have a written checklist of questions. You will want dates and places of births, marriages, divorces, education, occupations, military service, travels, adventures, achievements, unusual happenings, etc.

Your Living Link to Your Ancestors

When interviewing the older members of your family, your objectives will be far broader in scope because the memories and the memorabilia of your parents, aunts, uncles and grandparents can form the all-important bridge between you and the dis-

tant past. They will recount the narratives of their lives and times which always seem filled with so many heart-warming and dramatic adventures. They will also remember colorful traditions and stories related to them by their parents and grandparents which will take your research back to the 1800s.

We can't emphasize too strongly the importance of asking them to recall or to find among their old papers the essential facts or vital statistics of your ancestors' lives which you will need in your future research. A deceased person's primary vital statistics consist of three sets of data: the date and place of birth, the date and place of marriage, and the date and place of death. You will find that these statistics are the keys to the past which will open the doors into the lives of your ancestors in this country and in the countries of their origin.

Changes in Spelling of Family Names

While talking to your relatives, particularly the older members of your family, be sure to ask if they know of any changes which were made in the form or spelling of the names of your father, mother or any of your ancestors. It is essential that you know about these changes when tracing your ancestors.

There are many ways in which surnames became altered. Often careless and hurried port authorities and immigration clerks misspelled even the simplest names in their official records. Robertson became Robinson, and Schueller was spelled Schuler. Kurowski was misspelled Koroski, and Malloy became Molloy. Often, it was difficult to correct these errors at a later date.

Some newcomers shortened their names or changed the spelling to follow the accepted forms in this country. Smythe was altered to Smith; Llewellyn was changed to Lewellen; Porcellino was shortened to Porcello, Kovalenko to Koval.

Patterns of Research

While interviewing the members of your family and following up leads, you can also be pursuing other avenues of research. There are two other broad areas of genealogical information in this country: records-keeping organizations (governmental and institutional) and local sources either in your community or in the communities where your ancestors lived.

There is no predetermined order to follow in contacting these sources. It will depend on the type and amount of information you've been able to gather and evaluate from your family interviews and papers. Your common sense and ingenuity will indicate the directions which your research will take as the occasion arises. As you follow the clues in the search for your forefathers, you will find use for your instincts and intuitions as an amateur detective, investigative reporter, psychologist and author.

Tracing one's forefathers has been compared to fitting together the pieces of a jigsaw puzzle. Hopefully, each fact you discover about an ancestor will lead to other interlocking facts about that ancestor and about other ancestors. And as you fit them together, one after the other, the portraits of your ancestors and ancestresses will slowly take form before you.

The goal of the ancestor-searcher is to discover the pieces of the puzzle. You'll find that your imagination, good sense and perseverance will come into play. There will be frustrations, and there will be lucky gold mines of information contained in a single document or in the memory of an elderly relative. If you enjoy using your mind, you'll find the search for your forefathers to be a novel and intriguing recreation which knows no limitations and which is truly worthwhile in its rewards.

The chapters which follow are intended to be an introduction to the varied sources of genealogical records which are available to you. For your further study, you will find on page 23 a Bibliography of excellent guide books and reference books which are entirely devoted to the many aspects of genealogical research.

The Vital Importance of Vital Statistics

We have already pointed out the key role which the vital statistics of your ancestors will play in your future research in this country and abroad. For many centuries, church and civil offices have recorded or registered the dates and places of births, marriages and deaths. If you learn the date and place of any of these events in an ancestor's life, you can obtain a copy of the record for a fee by writing the official agency which is responsible for storing such records.

During the past 100 years, official records in this country have been kept quite systematically at the state and county levels. In prior years, the information recorded on vital statistics certificates varied considerably between different villages, towns, cities, counties and states.

For instance, some death certificates contain sparse information about the deceased while others list his or her full name, home address, age (sometimes the birth date), birthplace, cause of death, names of father and mother, name of spouse if married, attending physician, funeral home, cemetery and the name of the person supplying the information. Birth and marriage certificates list similar data relative to the event.

All of these valuable scraps of information can lead your research to the discovery of documents like wills, leases, service records, legal papers, divorce proceedings, school records, employment records, etc. Also of great importance are the clues leading to the vital statistics of that ancestor's father, mother and spouse.

In your interviews and in your records' research, you should always be on the alert for every fact or scrap of information about your first ancestors who immigrated to this country, whether they landed here in the 17th, 18th, 19th or 20th centuries. If you are to trace your ancestors in the lands of their origins, you must know the dates and the places of their births or marriages in the countries of their origin where these events were recorded.

Birth, Marriage and Death Records

The state and county offices which file these records have official titles which vary from state to state. To help you contact the proper office, the Department of Public Health Services has printed three booklets:

> *"Where to Write for Birth and Death Records"*
> *DHEW Publication No. PHS 76-1142*
>
> *"Where to Write for Marriage Records"*
> *DHEW Publication No. PHS 76-1144*
>
> *"Where to Write for Divorce Records"*
> *DHEW Publication No. PHS 76-1145*

You can obtain these booklets for $1.25 each from any Government Printing Office, GPO Bookstore or from the address below:

> *Superintendent of Documents*
> *U.S. Government Printing Office*
> *Washington, D C 20402*

When you write to the appropriate records office indicated in the PHS pamphlet, state your request simply and supply all pertinent details which will help the agency's personnel locate the record you are requesting among the hundreds of thousands of records on file. The name of your relative or ancestor must be spelled correctly, and it must be complete with the middle name or initial. It is not enough to list a state or a county as your ancestor's residence. You must know the town or city. Try to indicate the actual date or approximate date of the birth, death, marriage or divorce.

Enclose the fee indicated in the PHS booklet and a self-addressed, stamped envelope. Always include a self-addressed, stamped envelope in your letters requesting copies of records or replies from the agencies and individuals with whom you will be corre-

sponding. In some cases, they are an absolute requirement, and in all instances they are a gesture of courtesy which encourages cooperation.

Your request for a copy of a record might take this form:

> *Dear Sir:*
> *Please send me a copy of the death certificate of my grandfather, Thomas H. Carter. He lived at 2031 Roberts Avenue in Springfield, Illinois. He died in June or July, 1936. He was about 68 years old, and his wife's name was Edna. Enclosed is my check for $4 and a self-addressed stamped envelope. Thank you for your help.*

Federal Census Records

When you know the year an ancestor lived in a specific town or city, federal and state census records can supply you with interesting information about his or her life and family.

Since 1790, the United States has been conducting a nationwide census at ten-year intervals. This information is considered to be confidential for a period of 75 years after the dates when they were taken. Censuses from 1790 to 1900 are now available for public study, and some copies of later censuses can be viewed if you prove that your purpose is genealogical. Many of the 1890 census records were destroyed by a fire in 1921.

The National Archives in Washington is the custodian of census records which can be studied on microfilms at their Branch Offices which are located in Waltham, Mass., Bayonne, N.J., Philadelphia, Pa., East Point, Ga., Chicago, Ill., Kansas City, Mo., Fort Worth, Tex., Denver, Col., San Bruno, Cal., Laguna Niguel, Cal., and Seattle, Wash.

Census microfilms can also be viewed at many public and university libraries, genealogical and historical societies, and at all Branch Libraries of the Genealogical Society of Utah (see page 21). They can order films for your study for a small fee.

Many of the census listings were not made alphabetically. They were listed according to the wards and streets as the census-takers made their rounds. If your ancestor lived in a large city, it will help to have some idea of his or her address to find his or her listing. Of course, there are many places where an ancestor's address might appear: a birth certificate, newspaper obituary, legal document, etc.

Millions of records of genealogical interest are stored in the National Archives. They are cataloged in the **Guide to Genealogical Records in the National Archives (GS 4.6/ 2: G28)** which you can obtain for $2.50 at the nearest Government Printing Office or GPO Bookstore, or by writing to this address:

> Superintendent of Documents
> U.S. Government Printing Office
> Washington, D C 20402

Military Service Records

If your ancestor served in the armed forces prior to 1914, his records are stored in the National Archives, and you can obtain a copy of them. The address:

> **The National Archives and Records Service**
> Washington, D C 20408

First write to them for GSA Form 6751. On this form, fill in as much of the following information as possible: name of the veteran, dates and places of birth and death, the state in which he enlisted, the war in which he fought, his military unit. They will make a reasonable search and send copies of all papers concerning his enlistment.

If your ancestor or relative served in the armed forces after 1914, his records are covered by the Protection of Privacy Act. Usually, you will be sent copies of records if you can prove that you're a relative of the veteran and that the purpose of your request is genealogical. You can obtain the required application form (Form 180—Request Pertaining to Military Personnel) at this address:

> **National Personnel Records Center**
> General Services Administration
> 9700 Page Boulevard
> St. Louis, MO 63132

Naturalization Records

Two possible sources of your ancestors' vital statistics are their naturalization records and the passenger lists of the ships which brought them to this country.

Laws were passed in 1790 stating that any alien who desired citizenship should apply to any federal, state or county court for naturalization. As you would expect, the information contained in the records varies widely although they all list the person's name, age, occupation and place of origin. Some of the naturalization papers are still held in the courts where they were originally filed, while others have been transferred to the National Archives.

You can either try to locate the court where your ancestor was naturalized, or you can request the Archives to make a search by filling in GSA Form 7111 (the same Form used to apply for a search of Ship Passenger Lists) which you can obtain by writing to this address:

> National Archives
> NNC
> Washington, D C 20408

Since 1906 naturalization papers have been filed at the Immigration and Naturalization Service. You can apply for a search on Form G-641 which you can obtain by writing this address:

> Immigration and Naturalization Service
> 119 D Street, N.E.
> Washington, D C 20536

However, if your ancestor was naturalized in one of the five boroughs of New York City between 1790 and 1906, his citizenship papers are stored at the Federal Records Center in New Jersey. They will conduct a search if you send them your ancestor's full name and approximate date of naturalization. The address:

Federal Records Center
Military Ocean Terminal, Building 22
Bayonne, New Jersey

Ships' Passenger Lists

Among the millions of records stored in the National Archives are microfilms of passenger lists of ships arriving in Atlantic and Gulf of Mexico ports since 1820. There is a 50-year restriction to protect the privacy of immigrants still living. Passenger lists prior to 1930 are now available.

There are time gaps between some lists, and the listings themselves are sketchy and inconsistent. However, most of them show the passenger's name, age, occupation and the town of his origin or place of residence. This last piece of information can lead to all-important documents like his birth certificate, marriage license, etc., in his native land.

The facts needed to find your ancestor's passenger record are the name of the ship which brought him to this country as well as the port and approximate date (even the year) of its arrival. If you can discover any two of these facts, it will suffice.

With this information, you can request the National Archives to make a search of their files. Your request should be made on GSA Form 7111 which can be obtained by writing this address:

National Archives
NNC
Washington, D C 20408

You can make your own search by asking a public library or LDS Branch Library to obtain a microfilm of the appropriate Ship Passenger List which you can study on their premises.

Research in Communities of Your Ancestors

From your family interviews, old family papers and vital statistics' records, you will learn a great deal about the lives of your ancestors. In the communities where your forefathers lived, you will also find a variety of sources of information of a highly personal as well as official nature. This is especially true of small cities and towns, but it also applies to large cities.

Space will not permit us to describe the diversity of agencies, offices, institutions and societies which you will be contacting either in person or by letter. The guide books listed in the Bibliography will give you detailed advice on these subjects. In these pages, we will suggest some of the sources of information found in most communities.

Your prime research objectives will be the Records or Clerk's Offices of town halls, city halls, court houses and county buildings as well as public libraries, local historical and genealogical societies, local and community newspapers, churches and cemeteries.

In the Records Office or Clerk's Office of town halls, city halls and courthouses, you can look for prior-to-1900 records of births, marriages, divorces and deaths. They also store a miscellaneous variety of court records, deeds, wills, land records, taxpayer lists, licenses and documents of all kinds.

If librarians can find the time, they are extremely helpful in directing you to their genealogical guides and reference books, family histories, local history studies, out-of-print newspaper files, local military rosters, indexes of government reports, local biographical materials, etc. They can also tell you about local genealogical and historical societies whose members are experts on their subjects and whose files, especially their family histories, are fine sources of information.

Examining old newspaper files (often microfilmed) can reveal a wealth of information about activities in which your ancestor and his family might have participated, such as social affairs, religious ceremonies, graduations, political and business doings, court cases, accidents, births, weddings and every other event of human interest. Obituaries and death notices supply invaluable data about the deceased and his or her family.

Churches have records of births, baptisms, marriages and burials which often list parents, sponsors, witnesses and other attendants as well as the principal participants.

Cemetery records and tombstone inscriptions can give you an insight into family relationships which cannot be obtained from any other source.

Your research might lead you to social clubs, fraternal organizations, union headquarters, businessmen's associations, places of employment, and possibly old residents with long memories.

You'll find that doing this type of research in person will be far more effective than attempting to conduct a search by letter. However, if you can't visit the communities of your ancestors, you can write to the above sources and ask if they will be kind enough to look through their records for the information you are seeking. Be specific when giving them your dates and clues, and offer to pay them for their efforts in your behalf.

Prepared Family Histories

There are untold thousands of family histories or genealogies which individual ancestor-tracers have prepared and printed in the form of pamphlets and small booklets. If you can find such a history of your family, you have obviously discovered a gold mine.

Usually a family genealogist will have a limited number of copies printed for the members of his or her family, which are sometimes filed in local libraries, historical and genealogical societies. You can write to the libraries and societies in the community where your ancestor lived and ask if he or she is included in one of their family genealogies. You can also consult these sources:

Genealogical and Local History Books in Print, Volumes I and II. See the Bibliography on page 23.

Genealogies in the Libraries of Congress: A Bibliography. See page 23. The Library of Congress has 30,000 family histories in its files. On request, they will conduct a limited search.

Genealogies and Family Histories, A Catalog of Demand Reprints. University Microfilms International, 300 North Zeeb Road, Ann Arbor, Michigan 48106. If they have a copy of your family's history, they will supply you with photocopies on a fee-per-page basis.

General Church Distribution Center, 1999 West 1700 South, Salt Lake City, Utah 84104.

If you locate a family history done in your surname, you must have the proper vital statistics of your ancestor which will identify him or her as a member of that family.

The Genealogical Society of Utah

The Society possesses the largest and most famous collection of genealogical records in the world. Their vast and well-organized depository is called the Library of the Church of Latter Day Saints, the LDS Library or the Mormon Library. It is located at 50 East North Temple Street, Salt Lake City, Utah 84150.

In the Library's files are microfilmed records listing more than seventy million people, living and deceased, of all the countries of the world. Their six massive vaults contain more than one million rolls of films recording every type of genealogical information: baptisms, births, marriages, deaths, divorces, biographies, family histories, cemetery records, Bible records, censuses, archives collections, atlases, gazeteers, immigration records, naturalizations, newspaper obituaries, passenger lists, land records, *wills, probate records, tax lists, tombstone inscriptions, etc.*

The Society's records include information about men and women regardless of their religious affiliations, so they will probably have important documentation on one or more of your ancestors or family groups. Furthermore, the Mormons are non-political, and they have access to many genealogical records in Communist-dominated countries. Their files on the peoples of East Germany, Poland, Czechoslovakia, Hungary and Yugoslavia are unequalled.

The Library is open to everyone, and the only fee is a nominal one for making photocopies of records. If you cannot visit the main Library, you can use the facilities of one of their 230 branch libraries. You can locate a convenient library by calling their nearest LDS church in your telephone book. Before making a trip to the library, write or phone to learn its visiting hours.

At the branch library, you will find microfilms indexing the contents of the main Library. The branch librarians, who are volunteers, will arrange for the loan of films from the Salt Lake City files. You will be notified when the films arrive, and you will then be able to study them on the machines in the branch library.

When you learn the vital statistics of a forefather, we recommend that you take advantage of the LDS ancestor-tracing service. The Society has three sets of records in which individual surnames have been filed: Computer File Index (CFI), the Temple Index Bureau (TIB) and the Family Group Records Archives (FGRA). For a small fee, they will search these files for the records listed under your surname. When you receive their report, you will have to determine if you are related to the people listed. This is an excellent way to determine if a history or genealogy has already been prepared for your family.

To request a search, you must fill out a form called a "Temple Ordinance Index Request" which you can purchase from an LDS branch library or by writing to this address:

*General Copies Distribution Center
1999 West 1700 South
Salt Lake City, Utah 84104*

The Society has amassed all these genealogical records for a very good reason. One of the fundamental beliefs of Mormonism is that the bonds of a family are everlasting, that they extend backward in time and forward into eternity. If a Mormon can name and identify an ancestor, he can act as a proxy for the conditional baptism of that ancestor in the Church of Jesus Christ of Latter Day Saints.

People tracing their ancestors are grateful to the Society for making their files available and for their other outstanding services such as the Pedigree Research Survey and the LDS Research Specialists in foreign countries.

Professional Genealogists

*You might find it advisable to employ the services of a professional genealogist recommended by a librarian or genealogical society in your ancestor's community. You can also request the **Board for the Certification of Genealogists** to recommend an experienced researcher in the vicinity. The Board's address is 1307 New Hampshire Avenue N.W., Washington, D C 20026.*

Some people also use the services of professional genealogists to make searches for their ancestors in specific archives, government offices and libraries whose files are especially rich in a wide range of genealogical materials. Among such sources might be the National Archives in Washington, State Archives, the LDS Library and libraries with extensive genealogical collections like the Newberry Library in Chicago and the New York Public Library.

In any case, you will be employing an experienced professional research person whose rates are commensurate with his or her talents. It is wise to first learn about

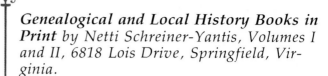

the hourly fees and the estimated cost of your assignment.

Genealogical Reference and Guide Books

Public libraries with genealogical divisions will have many of the guide and reference books listed below. Almost all libraries will have some of them, or they will be able to obtain them for you through the interlibrary loan service. The books marked with an asterisk (*) are recommended for beginners and can be purchased at most good book stores.

A Bibliography of Ship Passenger Lists, 1538–1825 by Harold Lancour, New York Public Library, 1963.

*A Guide to Foreign Genealogical Research by Maralyn Wellnauer, Milwaukee, Wisconsin, 1976.

A Handy Guide to Research Searching in the Larger Cities of the United States by E. Kay Kirkham, The Everton Publishers, Inc., Logan, Utah, 1965.

American Origins by L. G. Pine, Genealogical Publishing Co., Inc., Baltimore, Maryland, 1977.

Building an American Pedigree by Norman Edgar Wright, Brigham Young University Press, Salt Lake City, Utah, 1981.

Bureau of the Census Catalog of Publications, 1790–1972, U.S. Government Printing Office, Washington, D C, 1974.

*Don't Cry Timber by Prudence Groff Michael, Lakeville, Indiana, 1970.

*Finding Your Roots by Jean Eddy Westin, Ballantine Books, New York, 1977.

*Fundamentals of Genealogical Research by Laureen R. Jaussi and Gloria D. Chaston, Deseret Book Company, Salt Lake City, Utah, 1966.

Genealogical and Historical Societies by J. Konrad, Summit Publications, Munroe Falls, Ohio, 1979.

Genealogical and Local History Books in Print by Netti Schreiner-Yantis, Volumes I and II, 6818 Lois Drive, Springfield, Virginia.

Genealogical Research—Essentials by Norman E. Wright and David H. Pratt, Bookcraft, Inc., Salt Lake City, Utah, 1967.

Genealogical Research: Methods and Sources by Milton Rubicam and Jean Stephenson, American Society of Genealogists, Washington, D C, 1966.

Genealogical Source Handbook by George K. Schweitzer, Knoxville, Tennessee, 1981.

Genealogies in The Library of Congress: A Bibliography by Marion J. Kaminkow, Magna Carta Book Company, Baltimore, Maryland, 1972.

*Genealogy for Beginners by A. J. Willis, Genealogical Publishing Society, Baltimore, Maryland, 1970.

Guide to Records in the National Archives by M. B. Colket Jr. and Frank E. Bridges, National Archives, Washington, D C, 1964.

Guide to the Genealogical Records of the National Archives, Superintendent of Documents, U.S. Government Printing Office, Washington, D C, 20402, 1969.

Handbook for Genealogical Correspondence, The Everton Publishers, Inc., Logan, Utah, 1980.

Handy Index to the Holdings of the Genealogical Society of Utah by M. J. Brown, 3 volumes, Everton Publishers, Inc., Logan, Utah, 1980.

How to Find Your Family Roots by Timothy Field Beard and Denise Demong, McGraw-Hill Book Company, New York, 1977.

*How to Find Your Own Roots by Len Hilts, Cornerstone Library, New York, 1978.

How to Search a Cemetery, The Genealogical Institute, Salt Lake City, Utah, 1974.

*How to Trace Your Family Tree, American Genealogical Research Institute Staff,

Doubleday & Company, Inc., Garden City, New York, 1973.

Research in American Genealogy by E. Kay Kirkham, Deseret Book Co., Salt Lake City, Utah, 1962.

Search and Research by Noel C. Stevenson, Deseret Book Co., Salt Lake City, Utah, 1968.

*Searching For Your Ancestors by Gilbert H. Doane, University of Minnesota, Minneapolis, Minnesota, 1960.

The Genealogist's Encyclopedia by L. G. Pine, Weybright and Talley, New York, 1969.

*The Genealogy Beginner's Manual by Rick J. Aston, Peggy Tuck Sinko and Joseph C. Wolf, Newberry Library, Chicago, 1977.

The Handy Book for Genealogists by George B. Everton Sr., The Everton Publishers, Inc., Logan, Utah, 1965.

The Researcher's Guide to American Genealogy by Val D. Greenwood, Genealogical Publishing Co., Baltimore, Maryland, 1973.

Canadian Sources of Genealogical Records

The Public Archives of Canada have published a concise and informative booklet entitled **Tracing Your Ancestors in Canada**. You can obtain this excellent 36-page book, free of charge, by writing to the Archives. The address:

Public Archives of Canada
395 Wellington Street
Ottawa, Ontario, K1A ON3.

This well-organized booklet is a thorough introduction to the sources of genealogical records in Canada. You will agree when you read the booklet's Table of Contents: Published Sources, Geographical Information, Specialized Guides, Biographies and Family Histories, Specialized Lists, Census Records, Records of Births, Marriages and Deaths, Provincial Offices, Acadian

Sources, Church Records, Parish Registers, Adoption Records, Marriage Bonds, Cemetery Recordings, Land Records, Land Petitions, Metis Land Claims, Patents, Deeds, Records of Land Titles, Assessment Rolls, Estate Records, Military and Naval Records, Immigration Records, Records of Naturalization and Citizenship, Loyalist Sources, Federal Government Information Banks, Addresses of Principal Archives.

The records stored in the Public Archives of Canada are comparable to those in the National Archives of the United States. For information about their files, write to this address:

Publication Division
Public Archives of Canada
Postal Station B
59 Sparks and Elgin
Ottawa, Ontario, K1A ON3

The Archives have microfilmed their extensive collections of genealogical and historical records, studies, indexes, censuses and maps. You can request any public library or institution recognized by the Archives to borrow these microfilms which you can then study on their premises.

The Genealogical Library of Utah has Branch Libraries in Canada where you can view the films you request from their magnificent collection.

Records of Births, Marriages and Deaths

Since the early years of Canadian history, the recording of births, marriages and deaths has been the responsibility of the various church denominations. It was not until the late 19th century that civil registration of vital statistics was undertaken as a provincial responsibility.

All of the provincial and territorial offices have gathered considerable records from the years preceding the dates which indicate when civil registration began. Copies of records can be obtained for a minimum fee.

Newfoundland: *Civil registration began in 1892.*
>Registrar of Vital Statistics
>Department of Health
>Confederation Building
>St. John's, Newfoundland, A1X 5T7

Nova Scotia: *Civil registration began in 1909.*
>Deputy Registrar General
>Department of Health
>PO Box 157
>Halifax, Nova Scotia, B3J 2M9

Prince Edward Island: *Civil registration began in 1906.*
>Director of Vital Statistics
>Department of Health
>PO Box 3000
>Charlottetown, Prince Edward Island,
>   C1A 7P1

New Brunswick: *Civil registration began in 1920.*
>The Registrar General
>Vital Statistics Division
>PO Box 6000
>Fredericton, New Brunswick, E3B 5H1

Quebec: *Civil registration began in 1926.*
>The Registrar General
>Population Register
>845 Avenue Joffre
>Quebec, Quebec, G1S 3L8

Ontario: *Civil registration began in 1869.*
>Deputy Registrar General
>MacDonald Block
>Queen's Park
>Toronto, Ontario, M7A 1Y5

Manitoba: *Civil registration began in 1882.*
>The Office of Vital Statistics
>Department of Health and Community
>   Services
>Room 104, Norquy Building
>401 York Avenue
>Winnipeg, Manitoba, R3C OP8

Saskatchewan: *Civil registration began in 1920.*
>Vital Statistics
>Department of Health
>3211 Albert Street
>Regina, Saskatchewan, S4S OA6

Alberta: *Civil registration began in 1898.*
>Division of Vital Statistics
>Department of Social Services and
>   Community Health
>10405 10th Avenue, 4th Floor
>Edmonton, Alberta, T5J OA6

British Columbia: *Civil registration began in 1872.*
>Division of Vital Statistics
>Ministry of Health
>Victoria, B.C., V8V 1X4

Yukon Territory: *Civil registration began in 1924.*
>Vital Statistics
>Government of the Yukon Territory
>PO Box 2703
>Whitehorse, Yukon Territory, Y1A 2C6

North West Territories: *Civil registration began in 1925.*
>Registrar of Vital Statistics
>PO Box 1320
>Yellowknife, North West Territories,
>   X1A 2L9

Church Records and Parish Registers

For church records of births (baptisms), marriages and deaths (burials), you must write the parish or mission district where the event occurred. The Public Archives holds some parish registers, as well as transcripts and microfilm copies of others.

The sources of information in the communities where your ancestors lived are similar to those in the United States (see page 20).

Provincial and Territorial Archives

These Archives have collections of historical and genealogical value for people seeking information about their ancestors who lived within their boundaries. They will also order microfilms at your request from The Public Archives in Ottawa.

Provincial Archives of Newfoundland
and Labrador
Colonial Building, Military Road
St. John's, Newfoundland, A1C 5T7

Public Archives of Nova Scotia
6016 University Avenue
Halifax, Nova Scotia, B3H 1W4

Public Archives of Prince Edward
Island
PO Box 7000
Charlottetown, Prince Edward Island,
C1A 7M4

Provincial Archives of New Brunswick
PO Box 6000
Fredericton, New Brunswick, E3B 5H1

Archives Nationales du Quebec
PO Box 10450
Sainte-Foy, Quebec, G1V 4N1

Archives of Ontario
77 Grenville Street, Queen's Park
Toronto, Ontario, M7A 1C7

Provincial Archives of Manitoba
200 Vaughan Street
Winnipeg, Manitoba, R3C OP8

Saskatchewan Archives Board
Regina Office
University of Regina
Regina, Saskatchewan, S4S OA2

Saskatchewan Archives Board
Saskatoon Office
University of Saskatchewan
Saskatoon, Saskatchewan, S7N OWO

Provincial Archives of Alberta
12845-102th Avenue, Edmonton
Alberta, T5N OM6

Provincial Archives of British
Columbia
Parliament Buildings
Victoria, British Columbia, V8V 1X4

Yukon Archives
PO Box 2703
Whitehorse, Yukon Territory, Y1A 2C6

Prince of Wales Northern Heritage
Centre
Department of Natural and Cultural
Affairs
Government of the North West
Territories

Yellowknife, North West Territories,
X1A 2L9

Genealogical Reference and Guide Books for Canada

Genealogical Society of the Church of Jesus Christ of Latter Day Saints, Series B., No. 3, 1977.

Canadian Genealogical Handbook by Eric Jonasson, Wheatfield Press, Winnipeg, Manitoba, 1976.

Searching for Your Ancestors in Canada by Eunice R. Baker, Heritage House, Ottawa, Ontario, 1976.

Tracing Your Ancestry in Canada, The Public Archives, Ottawa, Ontario, 1979.

Canadian Ethnic Groups Bibliography by Andrew Gregorovich, Toronto, Ontario, 1972.

Among the books recommended in **Tracing Your Ancestors in Canada** are the following:

Census Returns 1825 – 1871, Supply and Services Canada, Mail Order Service, Hull, Quebec.

County Atlases of Canada: A Descriptive Catalogue, Public Archives of Canada, 1970.

Dictionnaire genealogique des familles canadiennes by Cyprien Tauquay, 7 volumes, 1871–1890.

Guide du genealogiste: a la recherche le vos ancetres by Jeanne Gregoire, 1974.

In Search of Your Roots by Augus Baxter, 1978.

Australian Sources of Genealogical Records

In Australia, Canada and the United States, there are many similarities in the contents of genealogical records and in the official agencies, institutions and churches which store them.

During Australia's early history, records of birth, marriage and death were recorded and filed in the churches of the various religious denominations. To obtain copies of these records, you should make your request to the church where the event occurred.

Civil registry of vital statistics became the responsibility of the six States and the Northern Territory in the mid-19th century. It began in the Capital Territory (Canberra) in 1930. You can request copies of certificates from these registry offices:

New South Wales: *Records date back to 1856.*
  The Registrar-General
  Prince Albert Road
  2000 Sydney, New South Wales

Queensland: *Records date back to 1856.*
  The Registrar-General
  Treasury Building
  4000 Brisbane, B7, Queensland

South Australia: *Records date back to 1842.*
  The Principal Registrar
  Box 1351 H. GPO
  5001 Adelaide, South Australia

Tasmania: *Records date back to 1839.*
  The Registrar-General
  Box 875, GPO J
  7001 Hobart, Tasmania

Victoria: *Records date back to 1853.*
  Government Statist
  295 Queen Street
  3000 Melbourne, Victoria

Western Australia: *Records date back to 1841.*
  The Registrar-General
  Oakleigh Building
  22 St. George's Terrace
  6000 Perth, Western Australia

Northern Territory: *Civil records date back to 1874.*
  Registrar-General of Births, Deaths
    and Marriages
  PO Box 367
  5794 Darwin, Northern Territory

Australian Capital Territory: *Records date back to 1930.*
  The Registrar-General
  PO Box 1515
  Canberra City, Australian Capital Territory 2600

The Library of the Church of Jesus Christ of Latter Day Saints is located at this address:

  Genealogical Library
  Church of Jesus Christ of Latter Day
    Saints
  55 Greenwich Road, Greenwich
  Sydney, Australia

The National Archives and State Archives have extensive collections of genealogical materials, census indexes, immigration records, etc.

  National Archives of Australia
  71 Leichardt Street, Kingston
  Australian Capital Territory 2604
  Australia

West Australia:
  State Library, Archives Branch
  3 Francis Street
  6000 Perth, West Australia

South Australia:
  State Library, Archives Department
  North Terrace
  5001 Adelaide, South Australia

Queensland:
  Archives Office
  Wynnum Road, Cannon Hill
  4000 Brisbane, Queensland

Tasmania:
  State Library, Archives Department
  91 Murray Street
  7000 Hobart, Tasmania

Victoria:
  State Library, Archives Division
  403-324 Swanston Street
  3000 Melbourne, Victoria

New South Wales:
  State Library, Archives Department
  MacQuarie Street
  2000 Sydney, New South Wales

Genealogical Reference and Guide Books for Australia

A Genealogical History of Pioneer Families of Australia by Perseval C. Mowle, Sydney, J. Sands, 1942.

Ancestors for Australians by B. R. Blaze and Muriel E. Runtling, Genealogical Society of Victoria, Melbourne, 1974.

Descent, Society of Australian Genealogists, Surry Hills, New South Wales, 1968.

Guide to Genealogical Sources in Australia and New Zealand by Neil T. Hansen, Melbourne, 1961.

Major Genealogical Sources in Australia, LDS Research Paper, Series E, No. 2., Genealogical Society of the Church of Jesus Christ of Latter Day Saints, 1977.

The Genealogist, Australian Institute of Genealogical Studies, PO Box 89, Hampton, Victoria 3188, 1974.

Tracing Your Ancestors in Europe

In the following pages, we will briefly outline the main sources of vital statistics and genealogical records in thirty European countries.

Most European countries follow similar methods in storing vital statistics and genealogical information. However, there are considerable variations in their filing systems and the information which their records contain.

You will find that the sources of records and genealogical information are located in three general areas. Some records are stored in central agencies and archives located in a nation's capital and in its provincial capitals. Others are kept in the cities, towns and parishes where the documents were originally recorded. There are also state, university and public libraries which have stores of genealogical information which is both general and specific.

As you prepare to start the overseas search for your ancestors, let us remind you of four invaluable sources of help and information in this country.

First, we would like to re-emphasize the unique role which the Genealogical Society of Utah can play in your research. As we've pointed out on page 21, this Library contains the largest and most well-indexed collection of genealogical records in existence. These documents have been gathered from all countries of the world. They have been microfilmed, cataloged and made available for the study of people of all religious faiths.

There are more than two hundred Branch Libraries connected with the Mormon churches in the United States, Canada and Australia. These Branch Libraries will order microfilms which you request and which you can later view on the premises. The cooperative and knowledgeable librarians will also inform you about the services of their Research Specialists in foreign countries.

No matter where your research leads you, the files of the Mormon Library will be most helpful. This is particularly true in the Communist-dominated countries where it is difficult and sometimes impossible to obtain genealogical information. In many cases, this information has been collected by overseas representatives of the Mormon Library and is available on their microfilms.

Second, we cannot recommend too strongly that you visit your libraries (particularly those with genealogical sections) and take advantage of their genealogical guide books, indexes, reference materials, maps, gazeteers, etc. You'll find the librarians to be helpful and patient.

Third, be sure to visit your local genealogical societies. The knowledgeable members are genuinely kind with beginners. There seems to be an unofficial brotherhood and sisterhood among ancestor-hunters in which everyone shares their experience and know-how. You will probably find people with specific experience in the geographic area of your research, and their practical advice can be a godsend.

Fourth, if you wish to employ a professional research person, the Genealogical Society of Utah has representatives in most European countries. Other people who will know about research people abroad are librarians, genealogical society members, national tourist bureaus, information attaches of embassies and the Board for the Certification of Genealogists, 1307 New Hampshire Avenue, NW, Washington, D C 20036.

Clearly it is not within the scope of this book to list the hundreds of records-keeping agencies and institutions in the thirty countries of Europe. Nor is it possible to offer detailed advice on ancestor-hunting in these countries. However, we will suggest ideas to follow when preparing your overseas correspondence, inquiries and requests for records. We will also summarize the availability of ancestral records in each country, and we will recommend reference books which describe the accepted research methods to follow in each European country.

How to Request the Records of Your Ancestors From the Countries of Their Origin

Thanks to our great interest in tracing our ancestors, the records-keeping agencies in Europe are receiving a large volume of requests for copies of vital statistics' certificates. They all have backlogs of requests, so don't expect a quick reply to your letter. The people who will attempt to answer your letter follow routine procedures, so your request should be explicit and your information must be accurate. To expedite their reply, we suggest that you follow these simple and logical rules.

1. Make sure that you spell your ancestor's name as it was spelled in the records of his or her native land. If you have doubts about its accuracy, indicate alternate spellings.

2. Your ancestor's name should be complete: first name, middle name or middle initial, last name.

3. You should know the approximate date and place of an event in your ancestor's life which was officially recorded, i.e., his or her birth, marriage, military service, emigration, etc.

4. Check the Mormon Genealogical Society if you are unsure of the above information.

5. Do not be deterred from requesting an ancestor's record if your information is approximate or incomplete. It costs little in time or money to send a request, and there's always a chance that you will be lucky.

6. Submit your request in a legible handwritten or typed letter. Of course, the latter form is always preferred.

7. The information you send should be both concise and complete. Write in a style which is straightforward, businesslike and formal. Avoid slang or any expression which might be misinterpreted.

8. Your request should be written in the language of your ancestor's country. If you can't make the translation yourself, someone you know (a relative, clergyman, friend) may be able to translate your letter properly. Usually language teachers at high schools and colleges are happy to help. Or send your letter to the country's Embassy, Consulate General or National Tourist Bureau, and they will translate your letter and return it to you.

9. Do not enclose a fee with your first request unless you have up-to-the-minute information on the subject. Always indicate your willingness to pay for any legitimate charges. When you are informed of charges in their subsequent reply, obtain an International Bank Draft for a small fee at your local bank. It will be negotiable overseas.

10. Always enclose two International Reply Coupons in a self-addressed enve-

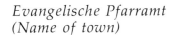

lope. You can purchase them at your local post office. These Coupons will expedite your reply by insuring air mail which takes one to two weeks, rather than one to three months. Needless to say, always use air mail in all your overseas correspondence.

Sources of Ancestral Records in Europe

Albania

Address of central archives:

> Archives D'Etat D'Albanie
> Tirana, Albania

Vital statistics' records were kept by Roman Catholic and Orthodox parishes until 1929 when Communists ordered them to be registered and filed by the civil authorities in each community. Most of the old records were incomplete, and many have been destroyed.

Austria

The present boundaries of Austria were established in 1918. In the past, Austria had been a great European power whose empire included parts of present-day Germany, Czechoslovakia, Poland, Yugoslavia, Italy and the Soviet Union. If you are seeking ancestors who lived in Austria before 1918, compare pre-World War 1 maps with modern maps to determine in which of the above countries they lived.

Prior to 1939, records of birth, marriage and death were kept by the various religious denominations. To obtain copies of these records, it is necessary to know the town or parish where the recorded events occurred. If your ancestor was a Roman Catholic, address your request to the rectory of his parish:

> Romanische Katholische Pfarramt
> (Name of town)

If your ancestor was a Protestant, write to the rectory:

> Evangelische Pfarramt
> (Name of town)

If he was a Jew, write to the Jewish Community Headquarters:

> Kulpts Gemeinde
> (Name of town)

Since 1939, records of vital statistics have been kept by local Bureaus of Vital Statistics called Standesamts in each town. In state capitals, vital statistics are kept by the Magistrat du Stadt.

You can write to the Austrian Embassy or a Consulate General's office for the address of the Standesamt or Magistrat du Stadt of your ancestor's community. The Embassy's address:

> Austrian Embassy
> 2342 Massachusetts Avenue NW
> Washington, D C 20008

There are seven State Archives in Vienna and one in Bregenz, Eisenstadt, Graz, Innsbruck, Klagenfurt, Leoben, Linz, Lodling and Salzburg.

RECOMMENDED GUIDES:

Handy Guide to Austrian Genealogical Records by Dagmar Senekovic. Everton Publishers, Logan, Utah, 1979.

Major Genealogical Sources in Austria, Series C, No. 16, Genealogical Society of Utah, Salt Lake City, Utah.

Germanic Genealogist, The Augustan Society, Torrance, California, 1976.

Belgium

If you draw an imaginary line just south of Brussels, you will find that the majority of people south of the line are French-speaking, and those north of the line are Flemish-speaking. Civil registration of births, marriages, divorces and deaths began in the 1790s.

To obtain vital statistics' records of an ancestor whose town is in the French-speaking region, write to this address:

Monsieur Le Sécrétaire Communal
Maison Communale
Zipcode (name of town)
Belgium

If the town is in the Flemish-speaking region, write to this address:

Mihnheer de Gemeentesekretaris
Gemeentehuis
Zipcode (name of town)
Belgium

Many records of genealogical importance (including vital statistics) are stored in the Regional Archives below.

Rijksarchief te Antwerpen
Door Verstraeteplaats 5
B-2000 Antwerpen (Antwerp)

Stadsarchief te Antwerpen
Venustraet 11
B-2000 Antwerpen

Rijksarchief te Brugge
Acadamiestraet 14
B-8000 Brugge (Bruges)

Archives de la Guerre
Place de la Vaillance 17
B-1000 Bruxelles (Brussels)

Rijksarchiefte Gent
Geraard de Duivelsteen
B-9000 Gent (Ghent)

Rijksarchief te Hasselt
Bampsplaan 4
B-3500 Hasselt

Rijksarchief te Kortrijk
Guido Gezzelestraet
B-8500 Kortrijk (Courtrai)

Archives de l'Etat a Liège
Rue Pouplin 8
B-4000 Liege

Archives de la Ville de Bruxelles
Hotel de Ville, Grand Place
B-1000 Bruxelles

Archives de l'Etat a Arlon
20 Avenue de la Gare
B-6700 Arlon

Archives de la Ville d'Arth
54 Rue de Pintamont
B-Arth

Archives de la Ville de Gand
13 Rue Abraham
B-9000 Gent (Ghent)

Stadarchief
Steeweg 1
B-2800 Mechelen

Archives de l'Etat de Mons
Place de Parc 23
B-7000 Mons

Archives de l'Etat a Namur
Rue d'Arquet 45
B-5000 Namur

Archives de l'Etat a Tournai
Rue de Sondart 12
B-7500 Tournai

We are informed that this organization specializes in genealogical research:

Service de Centralisation des Etudes
    Généalogiques et Démographiques
    de Belgique
Maison des Arts
Chaussée de Haecht 147
1030 Brussels, Belgium

RECOMMENDED GUIDES:

Major Genealogical Record Sources in Belgium, Series G, No. 3, Genealogical Society of Utah, Salt Lake City, Utah.

Be-Ne-Lux Genealogist, The Augustan Society, Torrance, California, 1977.

Bulgaria

There's little that we can tell you about the availability of vital statistics in this Communist republic. Civil registration began in Bulgaria in 1893. Older records (prior to 1893) are kept by the Ministry of Justice in Sofia.

Since the Communist take-over in 1946, people seeking information have not enjoyed much success. All records of birth, marriage and death are kept by the District People's Councils in the towns where they were filed. If you have the necessary information about your ancestor, write to the People's Council in his or her town and hope for the best.

The Central Archives of the State are located at this address:

> Centralen Darzaven Arhiv Na
>   Narodna Republika Balgarija
> Sofia, ul. Slavjanska, Bulgaria

Czechoslovakia

In 1918, the modern country of Czechoslovakia was pieced together from former regions of the Austro-Hungarian Empire: Bohemia, Moravia, Slovakia and parts of Silesia. Civil registration of births, marriages and deaths was instituted, but registration in churches was still permitted. The Soviet Union took control of Czechoslovakia in 1947, and all registrations were taken over by the state in 1950.

Today Czechoslovakia is the only Communist country which has an orderly procedure for handling requests for vital statistics' records. Requests should be made to this address:

> Consular Division
> Embassy of the Czechoslovak Socialist
>   Republic
> 3900 Linnean Avenue, N.W.
> Washington, D C 20008

The embassy will send you a pamphlet entitled **Information on Securing Family History from Czechoslovakia,** and they will forward your request to the Archives of the Ministry of the Interior in Prague. If a search is required, there is an hourly charge.

Older records are still stored by church parishes and town registry offices. For the locations of registries in Bohemia and Moravia, write to this address.

> Archivni Sprava
> Trida Obrancumiru 133
> Prague 6, Czechoslovakia

For registries in Slovakia, write to this office:

> Slovenska Archivni Sprava
> Vajanskeho
> Nabrezie 2,
> CS-800 Bratislava, Czechoslovakia

The Mormon Genealogical Society has extensive files on registries in Czechoslovakia, and the Cedok offices in New York should be consulted for up-to-the-minute information. Write to this address:

> Cedok-Czechoslovak Travel Bureau
> 10 East 40th Street
> New York, New York 10016

RECOMMENDED GUIDES:

Genealogical Research for Czech and Slovak Americans by Olga Miller, Gale Research, Book Tower, Detroit, Michigan, 1978.

Tracing Your Czech and Slovak Roots by M. A. Wellauer, 3239 N. 58th St., Milwaukee, Wisconsin, 1980.

Eastern European Genealogist, Augustan Society, Torrance, California, 1977.

Denmark

We strongly recommend that you write to the Danish Embassy and request that they send you an official Fact Sheet entitled **Tracing Your Danish Ancestors and Relatives.** This introduction to ancestor-hunting outlines the sources of genealogical and family records in Denmark. The address:

> Danish Embassy
> 3200 Whitehaven Street N.W.
> Washington, D C , 20008

Complete emigration records are stored at this address:

> Danes Worldwide Archives
> (Udvandrerarkivet)
> 2 Konvalve
> DK 9000 Alborg

Four provincial archives store a wealth of secular and religious documents including registrations of births, marriages and deaths.

> **Landsarkivet for Sjaelland, Lolland-Falster og Bornholm**
> 10 Jagtej
> DK-2200 Kobenhavn (Copenhagen),
>   Denmark

Landsarkivet for Fyn
36 Jernbanegade
DK-5000 Odense, Denmark

Landsarkivet for Norrejylland
5 L1. Sct. Hasgade
DK-8800 Viborg, Denmark

**Landsarkivet for Sonderjske Landele
(So. Jutland)**
45 Haderslevvej
DK-6200 Aabenraa, Denmark

Other records such as census indexes (dating back to 1787) and military draft lists (dating back to 1788) are stored at the National Archives:

Rigsarkivet
9 Rigsdagsgarden
DK 1218 Kobenhavn (Copenhagen)
Denmark

You'll find further genealogical information at the Royal Library:

Det Konglinge Bibliotek
8 Christians Brygge
DK 1218 Kobenhavn (Copenhagen)
Denmark

For ancestor-hunters, there's only one problem. The Danes, like the Swedes and Norwegians, did not institute the use of hereditary surnames until the late 19th century. Sons usually took the given name of their father and added -sen. For instance, Peter Olsen might name his son Anders Petersen. He in turn would call his son Ole Andersen. Thus there would be three different surnames in three generations. Two factors intensified the problem: there were few given names (so thousands of people shared the same surname), and many Scandinavians immigrating to this country changed the spelling of their names. Therefore, it is vitally important to know the exact spelling of your ancestor's name, and caution is required in tracing his name through the excellent records in Denmark.

RECOMMENDED GUIDES:

Genealogical Guidebook and Atlas of Denmark by Frank Smith and Finn A.

Thomsen, Everton Publishers, Logan, Utah, 1975.

Major Genealogical Sources in Denmark, Series D, Nos. 5-10, 16-19, Genealogical Society of Utah, Salt Lake City, Utah.

Danish Genealogical Research by J. G. Stevenson, 4 volumes, Provo, Utah, 1976.

England and Wales

We recommend that you write to the British Information Service and request their Genealogical Research Bulletin which will supply you with up-to-the-minute information on Britain's records sources. The address:

British Information Service
845 Third Avenue
New York City, New York 10022

As one would expect, the British record-keeping methods are logical and orderly. Certificates of births, marriages and deaths occurring since July 1, 1837 are filed at this address:

General Register Office
St. Catherine House, 10
London WC28 6JP, England

The fee for a copy of a certificate is £8.15p which includes airmail reply.

Records of baptisms, marriages and burials prior to 1837 are kept by parish churches of the various religious denominations.

Copies of divorce decrees can be obtained by writing to this office:

Chief Clerk
Divorce Registry, Room G45
Somerset House, Strand
London WC2R 1LP, England

For copies of wills, write to this address:

Principal Probate Registry of the
Family Division
Somerset House, Strand
London WC2B 1LP, England

continued on page 344

Our Family Biographies

Our Courtship

Place Photo Here

Our Names David Daniel Turenn
Louise Imogene Cushey

When and Where We Met at California State Teachers College
in the fall of 1944

Our First Date January, 1945

Our First Gifts Red Roses and Candy

The Proposal Dave asked my father if he could marry me.
He proposed to me on his knees.

Date of Our Engagement June, 1947

Memorable Recollections We enjoyed many of the movies of the era.
When in the Women's Dormitory, I would let down a
rope and he would send up a bag of food
to my room mate, Eunie Sproul and me.
— the dancing in the Provincial Room.

Our Wedding

Place Photo Here

Husband's Name _David Daniel Durinzi_

Wife's Maiden Name _Louise Imogene Cushey_

Date and Place of the Ceremony _August 27, 1947_
Venetia's Methodist Church

We Were Joined in Marriage by _Rev. Jenkins_

Best Man _Fred Adams_

Maid of Honor _Eunice Sproul_

Date and Place of Honeymoon _Aug 27-29 Ohiopyle_

Location of Marriage Certificate _Dresser drawer_

Memorable Recollections _We had our wedding breakfast at_
Sweeney's Restaurant.

Biography of the Wife

You'll find that writing the story of your life is far easier than you ever thought it would be. And when you look back over the events of your life, you'll relive the half-forgotten times of true happiness, fulfillment and achievement which have made your life worthwhile and important to those around you. As you reminisce about your own life and its meaning, you'll remember with fondness all the people whose lives you've touched and enlightened.

As we've previously suggested, it is best to first write a draft of your life story on notepaper before entering it in pen and ink on these pages. This will be a wise procedure when writing the other biographies in this Heritage book.

Place Photo Here

Name *Louise Irvin* Date 7/25/2020

Full Maiden Name *Louise Imogene Cushey*

Birth Date: Month *Oct* Day *17* Year *1926*

City *Hackett*

State *Pa*

Country *Washington*

Color Hair *Blonde* Eyes *Brown cat eyes*

Occupation *Mother' Helper at $5.00 per week*
Waitress at Sun Drug Store 40¢ an hour
Sales Clerk at Kaufman's Dept Store on Fifth Av
in Pgh $40 a week. Street car from Finley week to
Pgh 25¢
Waitress working my way thru
Calif State Teachers' College now a
University of Calif, Calif, Pa.
Senior High Teacher at Pleasant Hill
High School. Head of English Dept

40

Cooked the plays

Date

Place Photo Here

Biography of the Husband

Your biography will serve as a pattern to follow for the other biographies in this book. Therefore, we suggest that you first outline the story of your life on notepaper before actually recording it in this book. After you have arranged the various events and episodes in proper order, you can then expand or shorten them as you see fit.

We also suggest that you write in an easy, informal and concise style. Start with the first recollections of your childhood, and then proceed with the memorable events of your school years, young adulthood, your occupations, adventures and achievements. Be sure to leave plenty of space to write about the happy days to come.

Place Photo Here

Date _2020 Deceased_

Full Name _David Daniel Turinzi_

Birth Date: Month _June_ Day _28_ Year _1924_

City _Republic, Pa_

State _Pa_

Country _Fayette_

Color Hair _Black_ Eyes _Brown_

Occupation _School Teacher + Coach_

Date

Place Photo Here

Our Children

*On these pages, you will be able to keep alive the wonderful memories of your children's infancy and early childhood. Here, you will proudly record the dates and places of their births, their weights and lengths, the dates when they first laughed, crawled, stood up and spoke their first word. You can describe their delightful mannerisms, adventures and achievements. These are the first years which are so important in the future lives of your children. And so are the growing-up years which you can record in the **Family Memories** of this book.*

Place Photo Here

Name _____ Date _____

Child's
Full Name *Karen Lynne Turner*

Birth Date: Month *april* Day *16* Year *1952*

Hour *Almost* Min. *midnight — I wanted april 17 as I'm Oct 17*

Length _____ Weight _____

Hospital *Uniontown*

Doctor *All of this is in her baby book*

City _____

State _____

Country _____

Treasured Moments _____

Child's
Full Name _David Daniel Guerin_
Birth Date: Month _Jan_ Day _6_ Year _1956_
Hour _____ Min. _____
Length _____ Weight _____
Hospital _____
Doctor _____
City _____
State _____
Country _____
Treasured Moments

Just made it to hospital as I had him in 15 minutes

Place Photo Here

Name _____ Date _____

Child's
Full Name _____

Birth Date: *Month* ____ *Day* ____ *Year* ____

Hour _____ *Min.* _____

Length _____ *Weight* _____

Hospital _____

Doctor _____

City _____

State _____

Treasured Moments _____

_____

_____

_____

_____

_____

_____

_____

Name _____ *Date* _____

Place Photo Here

Child's
Full Name _____

Birth Date: Month _____ Day _____ Year _____

Hour _____ Min. _____

Length _____ Weight _____

Hospital _____

Doctor _____

City _____

State _____

Treasured Moments _____

_____

_____

_____

_____

_____

_____

_____

Name _____ Date _____

Place Photo Here

Place Photo Here

Place Photo Here

Name _____ Date _____   Name _____ Date _____

Child's
Full Name _____   _____

Birth Date: *Month* ____ *Day* ____ *Year* ____   _____

Hour _____ *Min.* _____   _____

Length _____ *Weight* _____   _____

Hospital _____   _____

Doctor _____   _____

City _____   _____

State _____   _____

Country _____   _____

Treasured Moments _____   _____

_____   _____

_____   _____

_____   _____

_____   _____

_____   _____

_____   _____

_____   _____

Child's
Full Name _____

Birth Date: Month _____ Day _____ Year _____

Hour _____ Min. _____

Length _____ Weight _____

Hospital _____

Doctor _____

City _____

State _____

Country _____

Treasured Moments _____

_____

_____

_____

_____

_____

_____

_____

_____

_____

Name _____ Date _____   Name _____ Date _____

Place Photo Here   Place Photo Here

Biography of the Wife's Mother

Probably, the biography which you will most enjoy writing will be the life story of your mother. You will, of course, write about the dates, happenings and experiences in her life which she would like to have remembered. Equally important are the personal and intimate insights into her character and personality: her spiritual values, her outlook on life, the things which she feels are important, her strengths and her loyalties, her hobbies and treasures.

Recall, too, the memorable and precious moments you have shared with her and which have meant so much to both of you.

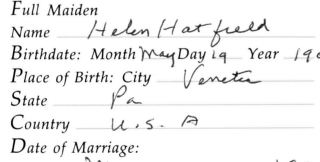

Place Photo Here

Date _____ 2020 _____

Full Maiden
Name _____ Helen Hatfield _____
Birthdate: Month May Day 19 Year 1908
Place of Birth: City _____ Venetia _____
State _____ Pa _____
Country _____ U.S.A _____
Date of Marriage:
Month _____ May _____ *Year* 1926
Place of Marriage: City _____
State _____
Country _____ U.S.A _____
Occupation _____ Student at _____
_____ Washington & Jefferson College _____

Name _____   Date _____

Place Photo Here

Biography of the Husband's Mother

Place Photo Here

It is said that a mother shows her son a part of her heart that no one else knows. If possible, you will want to sit down with your mother and write her biography together. You will want to record all the important events and moments of her childhood, teenage and school years, her marriage and her achievements as an adult woman and mother.

As you record the events of her life, remember to bring out the personality of the woman who shaped your life and your values with her gentleness and her strength, her steadfast devotion and unquestioning love.

Date _____

Full Maiden Name _____ Rose Maroney Durnin

Birth Date: Month _____ Day _____ Year _____

City _____

State _____

Country _____ U.S.A

Occupation _____ Housewife

Date of Marriage: Month _____ Day _____ Year _____

Place of Marriage: City _____

State _____

Country _____

Date

Place Photo Here

Biography of the Wife's Father
in Law

Place Photo Here

We're sure that recording the biography of your father in this Heritage Book will be a happy occasion for you.

Hopefully you can spend an evening with him while he reminisces about the favorite memories, stories and experiences of his youth and his later years as a husband and father. You will also want to write about the memorable times you've spent together, and the special bond of affection and understanding between you.

Of course you might ask him to write his own biography which you can then embellish to your heart's content.

Date _____

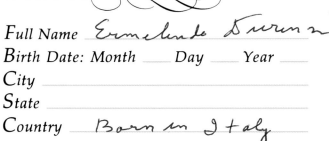

Full Name _Ermelindo Turin_

Birth Date: Month _____ Day _____ Year _____

City _____

State _____

Country _Born in Italy_

Name _____   Date _____

Place Photo Here

Biography of the Husband's Father

Place Photo Here

When you write the biography of your father and all the other biographies in this book, you will naturally record all the important dates and events in their lives which they feel are noteworthy.

Also be sure to describe the personal aspects of their lives: their appearance and mannerisms, their likes and dislikes, their sense of humor, the things they treasure, the ideas they value, everything that makes up each person's individuality and character.

When you write about your father in this way, you will portray the man of whom you are so proud and so fond.

Date _____

Full Name *Ermelado Durinz*

Birth Date: Month *June* Day *13* Year ____

City _____

State _____

Country *Italy*

Date _____

Place Photo Here

Our Children's Weddings

The wedding of a daughter or a son is always one of the most memorable and happy events in the history of every family.

You'll be able to record on these pages all the highlights of each of those joyous days: the date and place of the ceremony, the name of the clergyman or official performing the service, the names of the best man,

maid of honor, bridesmaids, ushers, guests and, of course, the names of the parents.

You can also describe the ceremony itself and the reception, toasts, dancing, tossing the bridal bouquet and everything else you would like to have remembered, including the honeymoon travels of the newlyweds.

Husband's
Name _____

Birth Date _____

Wife's
Maiden Name _____

Birth Date _____

Date of Ceremony _____

Place of Ceremony _____

_____

City _____

State _____

Married By _____

_____

Best Man _____

_____

Maid of
Honor _____

_____

Comments _____

_____

_____

Husband's
Name _____

Birth Date _____

Wife's
Maiden Name _____

Birth Date _____

Date of Ceremony _____

Place of Ceremony _____

_____

City _____

State _____

Married By _____

_____

Best Man _____

_____

Maid of
Honor _____

_____

Comments _____

_____

_____

Husband's
Name _____

Birth Date _____

Wife's
Maiden Name _____

Birth Date _____

Date of Ceremony _____

Place of Ceremony _____

City _____

State _____

Married By _____

Best Man _____

Maid of
Honor _____

Comments _____
_____
_____
_____
_____
_____
_____
_____
_____
_____
_____
_____
_____
_____
_____
_____
_____

Husband's
Name _____

Birth Date _____

Wife's
Maiden Name _____

Birth Date _____

Date of Ceremony _____

Place of Ceremony _____

City _____

State _____

Married By _____

Best Man _____

Maid of
Honor _____

Comments _____
_____
_____
_____
_____
_____
_____
_____
_____
_____
_____
_____
_____
_____
_____
_____
_____

Husband's
Name _____

Birth Date _____

Wife's
Maiden Name _____

Birth Date _____

Date of Ceremony _____

Place of Ceremony _____

_____

City _____

State _____

Married By _____

_____

Best Man _____

_____

Maid of
Honor _____

_____

Comments _____

_____

_____

_____

_____

_____

_____

_____

_____

_____

_____

_____

_____

_____

_____

Husband's
Name _____

Birth Date _____

Wife's
Maiden Name _____

Birth Date _____

Date of Ceremony _____

Place of Ceremony _____

_____

City _____

State _____

Married By _____

_____

Best Man _____

_____

Maid of
Honor _____

_____

Comments _____

_____

_____

_____

_____

_____

_____

_____

_____

_____

_____

_____

_____

_____

_____

Our Grandchildren

Grandparents have always known that their happy and heaven-sent duty was to spoil their little grandchildren, and now modern research supports this ancient tradition. On these pages, you can feel free to write about your own miraculous grandchildren: their enchanting smiles and bewitching charms, the wonderful wit and wisdom which you can see in their eyes even before they can speak a word. Somehow you know that the little ones understand and respond to your love. These are priceless moments which you can recapture here and in the pages of **Family Memories**.

Place Photo Here

Name _____ Date _____

Child's
Full Name _____

Birth Date: Month ____ Day ____ Year ____

Hour _____ Min. _____

Length _____ Weight _____

Hospital _____

Doctor _____

City _____

State _____

Treasured Moments _____

_____

_____

_____

_____

_____

_____

Child's
Full Name _____

Birth Date: Month _____ Day _____ Year _____

Hour _____ Min. _____

Length _____ Weight _____

Hospital _____

Doctor _____

City _____

State _____

Treasured Moments _____

_____

_____

_____

_____

_____

_____

_____

_____

_____

_____

_____

_____

_____

_____

_____

_____

_____

_____

_____

_____

Place Photo Here

Name _____ Date _____

_____

_____

_____

_____

_____

_____

_____

_____

_____

_____

_____

_____

_____

_____

Child's
Full Name _____

Birth Date: Month ___ *Day* ___ *Year* ___

Hour _____ *Min.* _____

Length _____ *Weight* _____

Hospital _____

Doctor _____

City _____

State _____

Treasured Moments _____

_____

_____

_____

_____

_____

_____

Name _____ *Date* ___

Place Photo Here

Child's
Full Name _____

Birth Date: Month _____ *Day* _____ *Year* _____

Hour _____ *Min.* _____

Length _____ *Weight* _____

Hospital _____

Doctor _____

City _____

State _____

Treasured Moments _____

_____

_____

_____

_____

_____

Name _____ *Date* _____

Place Photo Here

Place Photo Here

Place Photo Here

Name _____ Date _____

Child's
Full Name _____

Birth Date: Month _____ Day _____ Year _____

Hour _____ Min. _____

Length _____ Weight _____

Hospital _____

Doctor _____

City _____

State _____

Treasured Moments _____

_____

_____

_____

_____

_____

_____

_____

_____

_____

_____

Name _____ Date _____

Child's
Full Name _____

Birth Date: Month _____ Day _____ Year _____

Hour _____ Min. _____

Length _____ Weight _____

Hospital _____

Doctor _____

City _____

State _____

Treasured Moments _____

_____

_____

_____

_____

_____

_____

_____

_____

_____

Child's
Full Name _____

Birth Date: *Month* ____ *Day* ____ *Year* ____

Hour _____ *Min.* _____

Length _____ *Weight* _____

Hospital _____

Doctor _____

City _____

State _____

Treasured Moments _____

_____

_____

_____

_____

_____

_____

_____

_____

Name _____ *Date* _____

Child's
Full Name _____

Birth Date: *Month* ____ *Day* ____ *Year* ____

Hour _____ *Min.* _____

Length _____ *Weight* _____

Hospital _____

Doctor _____

City _____

State _____

Treasured Moments _____

_____

_____

_____

_____

_____

_____

_____

_____

Name _____ *Date* _____

Place Photo Here

Place Photo Here

Wife's Sisters and Brothers and Their Spouses

Place Photo Here

Our sisters and brothers, regardless of their ages, were the companions and play-mates of our childhood and our youth. They were the laughing and bickering con-fidants of our school years, and today they are the loyal and steadfast friends of our maturity.

You'll find it difficult to crowd into these pages all the memorable dates and events in the lives of your brothers and sisters and their wives and husbands. In the **Family Memories** there are thirty-three chapters where you can write about the happy mo-ments and the important times which you've shared with them.

Name _____ Date _____

Full Name _____

Spouse _____

Birth Date: Month ____ Day ____ Year ____

City _____

State _____

Relation _____

Comments _____

Full Name _____
Spouse _____
Birth Date: Month _____ Day _____ Year _____
City _____
State _____
Relation _____
Comments _____
_____
_____
_____
_____
_____
_____
_____
_____
_____
_____
_____
_____
_____
_____
_____
_____
_____
_____

Place Photo Here

Name _____ Date _____

Full Name _____
Spouse _____
Birth Date: Month _____ Day _____ Year _____
City _____
State _____
Relation _____
Comments _____
_____
_____
_____
_____
_____
_____
_____
_____

Full Name

Spouse

Birth Date: Month   Day   Year

City

State

Relation

Comments

Full Name

Spouse

Birth Date: Month   Day   Year

City

State

Relation

Comments

Name   *Date*

Place Photo Here

Full Name _____
Spouse _____
Birth Date: Month _____ *Day* _____ *Year* _____
City _____
State _____
Relation _____
Comments _____
_____
_____
_____
_____
_____
_____

Name _____ *Date* _____

Place Photo Here

Full Name _____
Spouse _____
Birth Date: Month _____ *Day* _____ *Year* _____
City _____
State _____
Relation _____
Comments _____
_____
_____
_____
_____
_____
_____
_____
_____
_____
_____
_____
_____
_____
_____
_____
_____
_____
_____
_____
_____
_____

Husband's Sisters and Brothers and Their Spouses

Place Photo Here

Name _____ Date _____

You'll be able to record on these pages the life stories of your sisters and brothers with whom you share so many vivid and unforgettable memories of your childhood and youth. You stood staunchly together during the trials of your growing-up years, and you shared one another's secrets and triumphs. No matter how far apart you live today, no one else will ever take their places in your affections and your thoughts.

Here you can write all about their lives as well as the lives of their husbands and wives. You'll find more space to write about them in the **Family Memories** chapters.

Full Name _____

Spouse _____

Birth Date: Month _____ Day _____ Year _____

City _____

State _____

Relation _____

Comments _____

Full Name _____

Spouse _____

Birth Date: Month _____ *Day* _____ *Year* _____

City _____

State _____

Relation _____

Comments _____

_____

_____

_____

_____

_____

_____

_____

_____

_____

_____

_____

_____

_____

_____

_____

_____

_____

_____

_____

Place Photo Here

Name _____ *Date* _____

Full Name _____

Spouse _____

Birth Date: Month _____ *Day* _____ *Year* _____

City _____

State _____

Relation _____

Comments _____

_____

_____

_____

_____

_____

_____

_____

_____

_____

Full Name _____

Spouse _____

Birth Date: Month _____ Day _____ Year _____

City _____

State _____

Relation _____

Comments _____

_____

_____

_____

_____

_____

_____

_____

_____

Name _____ Date _____

Place Photo Here

Full Name _____

Spouse _____

Birth Date: Month _____ Day _____ Year _____

City _____

State _____

Relation _____

Comments _____

Full Name

Spouse

Birth Date: Month   Day   Year

City

State

Relation

Comments

Full Name

Spouse

Birth Date: Month   Day   Year

City

State

Relation

Comments

Name _____ *Date* _____

Place Photo Here

Aunts and Uncles of the Wife

*O*ften, the aunts and uncles in a closely-knit family group play important parts in the lives of their nieces and nephews, especially during their formative years of childhood and youth. Usually we have favorite aunts and uncles whose affection and concern for us will endure and grow stronger through the years.

On these pages, you can record the stories of their lives. You might ask them to outline their own biographies, and you can then add the happy experiences and memories which you have shared with them.

Full Name _____

Spouse _____

Birth Date: Month _____ *Day* _____ *Year* _____

City _____

State _____

Relation _____

Comments _____

_____

_____

_____

_____

Place Photo Here

Name _____ *Date* _____

Full Name _____
Spouse _____
Birth Date: Month _____ Day _____ Year _____
City _____
State _____
Relation _____
Comments _____
_____
_____
_____
_____
_____
_____
_____
_____
_____
_____
_____
_____
_____
_____
_____

Place Photo Here

Name _____ Date _____

Full Name _____
Spouse _____
Birth Date: Month _____ Day _____ Year _____
City _____
State _____
Relation _____
Comments _____
_____
_____
_____
_____
_____
_____
_____
_____
_____

Full Name _____

Spouse _____

Birth Date: Month _____ Day _____ Year _____

City _____

State _____

Relation _____

Comments _____

_____

_____

_____

_____

_____

_____

Name _____ Date _____

Full Name _____

Spouse _____

Birth Date: Month _____ Day _____ Year _____

City _____

State _____

Relation _____

Comments _____

_____

_____

_____

_____

_____

_____

_____

_____

_____

_____

_____

_____

_____

_____

_____

Place Photo Here

Full Name _____
Spouse _____
Birth Date: Month _____ *Day* _____ *Year* _____
City _____
State _____
Relation _____
Comments _____

_____
_____
_____
_____
_____
_____
_____

Name _____ *Date* _____

Place Photo Here

Full Name _____
Spouse _____
Birth Date: Month _____ *Day* _____ *Year* _____
City _____
State _____
Relation _____
Comments _____

Aunts and Uncles of the Husband

Place Photo Here

In many families, the influence of aunts and uncles in the lives of their nephews and nieces is second only to the parents. Some of them seem to be indispensable parts of our lives, and we associate them with many of the experiences and occasions which we remember most fondly.

When you record their life stories, describe the appearance, personalities and philosophies of these men and women to whom you owe so much. Remember that you can also write about them in the **Family Memories** chapters.

Full Name

Spouse

Birth Date: Month ____ Day ____ Year ____

City

State

Relation

Comments

Name _____ Date _____

Full Name _____

Spouse _____

Birth Date: Month _____ Day _____ Year _____

City _____

State _____

Relation _____

Comments _____

_____

_____

_____

_____

_____

_____

_____

_____

_____

_____

_____

_____

_____

_____

_____

_____

| Place Photo Here |

Name _____ Date _____

Full Name _____

Spouse _____

Birth Date: Month _____ Day _____ Year _____

City _____

State _____

Relation _____

Comments _____

_____

_____

_____

_____

_____

_____

_____

_____

Full Name _____

Spouse _____

Birth Date: Month _____ Day _____ Year _____

City _____

State _____

Relation _____

Comments _____

_____

_____

_____

_____

_____

_____

_____

Name _____ Date _____

Full Name _____

Spouse _____

Birth Date: Month _____ Day _____ Year _____

City _____

State _____

Relation _____

Comments _____

Place Photo Here

Full Name _____

Spouse _____

Birth Date: Month _____ *Day* _____ *Year* _____

City _____

State _____

Relation _____

Comments _____

_____

_____

_____

_____

_____

_____

_____

Name _____ *Date* _____

Full Name _____

Spouse _____

Birth Date: Month _____ *Day* _____ *Year* _____

City _____

State _____

Relation _____

Comments _____

_____

_____

_____

_____

_____

_____

_____

_____

_____

_____

_____

_____

_____

_____

_____

Place Photo Here

Nieces and Nephews of the Wife

It is wonderful to observe how often and how naturally an aunt will almost become a second mother to her nieces and nephews. Beginning on the day when she first holds the infant in her arms, an undemanding relationship of fondness and understanding can grow between them which will last the rest of their lives.

You can describe here the memorable happenings and achievements in the lives of your nieces and nephews, as well as their appearance, characteristics, talents and personalities.

Full Name

Spouse

Birth Date: Month   Day   Year

City

State

Relation

Comments

Place Photo Here

Name   Date

Full Name _____
Spouse _____
Birth Date: Month _____ Day _____ Year _____
City _____
State _____
Relation _____
Comments _____

_____
_____
_____
_____
_____
_____
_____
_____
_____
_____
_____
_____
_____
_____
_____
_____
_____
_____
_____
_____

Place Photo Here

Name _____ Date _____

Full Name _____
Spouse _____
Birth Date: Month _____ Day _____ Year _____
City _____
State _____
Relation _____
Comments _____

_____
_____
_____
_____
_____
_____
_____
_____
_____
_____

Full Name _____

Spouse _____

Birth Date: Month _____ *Day* _____ *Year* _____

City _____

State _____

Relation _____

Comments _____

_____

_____

_____

_____

_____

_____

_____

Name _____ *Date* _____

Full Name _____

Spouse _____

Birth Date: Month _____ *Day* _____ *Year* _____

City _____

State _____

Relation _____

Comments _____

_____

_____

_____

_____

_____

_____

_____

Place Photo Here

Full Name _____

Spouse _____

Birth Date: Month _____ *Day* _____ *Year* _____

City _____

State _____

Relation _____

Comments _____

_____

_____

_____

_____

_____

_____

_____

Name _____ *Date* _____

Place Photo Here

Full Name _____

Spouse _____

Birth Date: Month _____ *Day* _____ *Year* _____

City _____

State _____

Relation _____

Comments _____

_____

_____

_____

_____

_____

_____

_____

_____

_____

_____

_____

_____

_____

_____

_____

_____

_____

Nieces and Nephews of the Husband

Those of us who are lucky to live in the communities with our brothers or sisters often become an intimate part of the lives of their children. A heart-warming bond of affection and trust can grow between an uncle and a nephew or a niece which becomes a continuing source of pleasure for both of them.

On these pages you can describe the happy memories you've shared with your nieces and nephews, and you can write about the important dates, events and experiences of their lives.

Place Photo Here

Name _____ Date _____

Full Name _____

Spouse _____

Birth Date: Month _____ Day _____ Year _____

City _____

State _____

Relation _____

Comments _____

Full Name _____
Spouse _____
Birth Date: Month ____ Day ____ Year ____
City _____
State _____
Relation _____
Comments _____

_____
_____
_____
_____
_____
_____
_____
_____
_____
_____
_____
_____
_____
_____
_____
_____
_____
_____
_____
_____
_____
_____

Place Photo Here

Name _____ Date ____

Full Name _____
Spouse _____
Birth Date: Month ____ Day ____ Year ____
City _____
State _____
Relation _____
Comments _____

_____
_____
_____
_____
_____
_____
_____
_____
_____
_____
_____

Full Name _____
Spouse _____
Birth Date: Month ____ Day ____ Year ____
City _____
State _____
Relation _____
Comments _____

_____
_____
_____
_____
_____
_____
_____
_____
_____

Name _____ *Date* _____

Full Name _____
Spouse _____
Birth Date: Month ____ Day ____ Year ____
City _____
State _____
Relation _____
Comments _____

_____
_____
_____
_____
_____
_____
_____
_____
_____

Place Photo Here

Full Name _____

Spouse _____

Birth Date: Month _____ Day _____ Year _____

City _____

State _____

Relation _____

Comments _____

_____

_____

_____

_____

_____

_____

_____

_____

Name _____ *Date* _____

Full Name _____

Spouse _____

Birth Date: Month _____ Day _____ Year _____

City _____

State _____

Relation _____

Comments _____

_____

_____

_____

_____

_____

_____

_____

_____

_____

_____

_____

_____

_____

Place Photo Here

Cousins of the Wife

Some of our cousins are as much a part of our lives and our memories as our brothers and sisters, while others we see only at family reunions or holiday gatherings. It depends, of course, on the distance between our homes, and the closeness of our relationship to them when we were children.

Here you can describe your experiences together as young people and adults, and you can also record the dates and places of their births, their schools, occupations and professions, their marriages, children, activities and achievements.

Place Photo Here

Full Name _____

Spouse _____

Birth Date: Month ____ Day ____ Year ____

City _____

State _____

Relation _____

Comments _____

Name _____ Date _____

_____
_____
_____
_____
_____
_____
_____
_____
_____
_____
_____
_____
_____

Full Name _____

Spouse _____

Birth Date: Month _____ Day _____ Year _____

City _____

State _____

Relation _____

Comments _____
_____
_____
_____
_____
_____
_____
_____
_____
_____
_____
_____
_____
_____
_____
_____
_____
_____
_____
_____

Place Photo Here

Name _____ Date _____

Full Name _____

Spouse _____

Birth Date: Month _____ Day _____ Year _____

City _____

State _____

Relation _____

Comments _____
_____
_____
_____
_____
_____
_____
_____
_____

Full Name _____
Spouse _____
Birth Date: Month _____ Day _____ Year _____
City _____
State _____
Relation _____
Comments _____
_____
_____
_____
_____
_____
_____
_____

Name _____ Date _____

Place Photo Here

Full Name _____
Spouse _____
Birth Date: Month _____ Day _____ Year _____
City _____
State _____
Relation _____
Comments _____

Full Name

Spouse

Birth Date: Month _____ Day _____ Year _____

City

State

Relation

Comments

Full Name

Spouse

Birth Date: Month _____ Day _____ Year _____

City

State

Relation

Comments

Name _____ Date _____

Place Photo Here

Cousins of the Husband

Cousins come with a variety of titles: first cousins, second cousins, third cousins, cousins-once-removed, etc. Some of them are the intimate companions of our childhood and remain close friends through the years. Others we know only by name. Nevertheless they are all kinsmen and kinswomen and members of our family.

You can record their biographies and your memories of each of them on these pages and in the chapters of the **Family Memories** section of this Heritage Book.

Place Photo Here

Name _____ Date _____

Full Name _____

Spouse _____

Birth Date: Month _____ Day _____ Year _____

City _____

State _____

Relation _____

Comments _____

Full Name _____
Spouse _____
Birth Date: Month _____ Day _____ Year _____
City _____
State _____
Relation _____
Comments _____

_____
_____
_____
_____
_____
_____
_____
_____
_____
_____
_____
_____
_____
_____
_____
_____
_____
_____
_____

Place Photo Here

Name _____ Date _____

Full Name _____
Spouse _____
Birth Date: Month _____ Day _____ Year _____
City _____
State _____
Relation _____
Comments _____

_____
_____
_____
_____
_____
_____
_____
_____
_____
_____
_____
_____

Full Name _____
Spouse _____
Birth Date: Month _____ *Day* _____ *Year* _____
City _____
State _____
Relation _____
Comments _____
_____
_____
_____
_____
_____
_____
_____
_____

Name _____ *Date* _____

Full Name _____
Spouse _____
Birth Date: Month _____ *Day* _____ *Year* _____
City _____
State _____
Relation _____
Comments _____
_____
_____
_____
_____
_____
_____
_____
_____
_____
_____
_____
_____
_____
_____
_____
_____
_____
_____
_____

Place Photo Here

Full Name _____

Spouse _____

Birth Date: Month _____ Day _____ Year _____

City _____

State _____

Relation _____

Comments _____

_____

_____

_____

_____

_____

_____

_____

Name _____ Date _____

Full Name _____

Spouse _____

Birth Date: Month _____ Day _____ Year _____

City _____

State _____

Relation _____

Comments _____

Place Photo Here

Grandparents of the Wife

Usually our grandparents are the oldest and dearest members of our family whom we are privileged to know personally. Their memories are priceless sources of information about your other ancestors, and their own biographies will probably be among the most fascinating you will write in this Heritage Book.

Be sure to devote the time to interview them carefully about the dates, occupations and unusual experiences of their own lives and the lives of their parents and grandparents who are, of course, your great grandparents and great great grandparents.

Place Photo Here

Maternal Grandmother

Her Full
Name _____

Birth Date: Month ____ Day ____ Year ____

City _____

State _____

Country _____

Occupation _____

Date of
Marriage: Month ____ Day ____ Year ____

Place of
Marriage: City _____

State _____

Country _____

_____
_____
_____

Date _____

_____
_____
_____
_____
_____
_____
_____
_____
_____
_____
_____
_____

Maternal Grandfather

His Full
Name _____

Birth Date: Month _____ Day _____ Year _____

City _____

State _____

Country _____

Occupation _____

_____

_____

_____

_____

_____

_____

_____

_____

_____

_____

_____

_____

_____

Place Photo Here

Date _____

Paternal Grandmother

Her Full Name _____

Birth Date: Month _____ *Day* _____ *Year* _____

City _____

State _____

Country _____

Occupation _____

Date of Marriage: Month _____ *Day* _____ *Year* _____

Place of Marriage: City _____

State _____

Country _____

_____

_____

Date _____

Place Photo Here

Paternal Grandfather

*H*is Full
*N*ame _____

*B*irth Date: Month ___ Day ___ Year ___
*C*ity _____
*S*tate _____
*C*ountry _____
*O*ccupation _____

_____
_____
_____
_____
_____
_____

*D*ate _____

Place Photo Here

Grandparents of the Husband

In most cases, our grandparents were born in the early years of the 20th century. We tend to think of them as leading quiet, uncomplicated lives, without realizing that they were participants in the most momentous changes in world history. During their lifetimes, the dreams of the past became actual facts: automobiles, air travel, skyscrapers, motion pictures, television and space voyages. They even survived two World Wars and the Great Depression.

As you write the biographies of your grandparents, try to portray their roles and reactions to the challenging times in which they lived.

Maternal Grandmother

Her Full
Name _____

Birth Date: Month _____ Day _____ Year _____

City _____

State _____

Country _____

Occupation _____

Date of
Marriage: Month _____ Day _____ Year _____

Place of
Marriage: City _____

State _____

Country _____

_____
_____

Place Photo Here

Date _____

_____
_____
_____
_____
_____
_____
_____
_____
_____
_____
_____
_____
_____
_____
_____
_____
_____
_____

Maternal Grandfather

His Full
Name _____

Birth Date: Month _____ Day _____ Year _____

City _____

State _____

Country _____

Occupation _____

_____
_____
_____
_____
_____
_____
_____
_____
_____
_____
_____
_____
_____
_____
_____
_____
_____
_____
_____

Place Photo Here

Date _____

Paternal Grandmother

Her Full
Name _____

Birth Date: Month _____ Day _____ Year _____

City _____

State _____

Country _____

Occupation _____

Date of
Marriage: Month _____ Day _____ Year _____

Place of
Marriage: City _____

State _____

Country _____

_____

_____

_____

_____

Date _____

Place Photo Here

Paternal Grandfather

His Full
Name _____

Birth Date: Month _____ Day _____ Year _____

City _____

State _____

Country _____

Occupation _____

_____

_____

_____

_____

_____

_____

_____

_____

_____

Date _____

Place Photo Here

Great Grandparents of the Wife

Hopefully you will be able to obtain factual and personal information about your great grandparents either through interviews with grandparents, parents, uncles and aunts, or through normal genealogical research methods.

The lifetimes of most of our great grandparents spanned the years of the late 19th and early 20th centuries when this country enjoyed the contrasting ethics and tastes of Victorianism and lusty individualism. It will be interesting for you to keep these contrasts in mind as you record the details of your great grandfather's and great grandmother's lives on these pages.

Maternal Great Grandmother

Her Full
Name _____

Birth Date: Month _____ Day _____ Year _____

City _____

State _____

Country _____

Occupation _____

Date of
Marriage: Month _____ Day _____ Year _____

Place of
Marriage: City _____

State _____

Country _____

_____

Place Photo Here

Date _____

_____

_____

_____

_____

_____

_____

_____

_____

_____

_____

_____

_____

_____

_____

_____

_____

Maternal Great Grandfather

*H*is Full
Name _____

*B*irth Date: Month _____ Day _____ Year _____

*C*ity _____

*S*tate _____

*C*ountry _____

*O*ccupation _____

_____

_____

_____

_____

_____

_____

Place Photo Here

Date _____

Paternal Great Grandmother

*Her Full
Name* ....

Birth Date: Month .... *Day* .... *Year* ....

City ....

State ....

Country ....

Occupation ....

*Date of
Marriage: Month* .... *Day* .... *Year* ....

*Place of
Marriage: City* ....

State ....

Country ....

....

....

Date ....

Place Photo Here

Paternal Great Grandfather

His Full Name _____

Birth Date: Month _____ *Day* _____ *Year* _____

City _____

State _____

Country _____

Occupation _____

_____

_____

_____

_____

_____

_____

Date _____

Place Photo Here

Great Grandparents of the Husband

Your great grandparents lived in an era of excitement, expansion and optimism. In this country the Civil War had ended; millions of courageous immigrants were landing in our seaports; Indians still rode the plains, electricity lit the city streets; newcomers and natives surged westward; railroads spanned the continent; fortunes were made and lost on Wall Street.

It was a time of adventure and challenge, invention and hard work. You might feel a little envy for your great grandparents as you record the stories of their experiences, occupations and achievements in this book.

Maternal Great Grandmother

Her Full
Name _____

Birth Date: Month ____ Day ____ Year ____

City _____

State _____

Country _____

Occupation _____

Date of
Marriage: Month ____ Day ____ Year ____

Place of
Marriage: City _____

State _____

Country _____
_____

Place Photo Here

Date _____

_____

_____

_____

_____

_____

_____

_____

_____

_____

_____

_____

_____

_____

_____

_____

_____

_____

_____

Maternal Great Grandfather

His Full
Name _____

Birth Date: Month _____ Day _____ Year _____

City _____

State _____

Country _____

Occupation _____

_____

_____

_____

_____

_____

_____

_____

_____

_____

_____

_____

_____

_____

_____

_____

_____

_____

Place Photo Here

Date _____

_____

_____

_____

_____

_____

_____

_____

_____

_____

_____

_____

_____

_____

_____

_____

Paternal Great Grandmother

Her Full
Name _____

Birth Date: Month _____ Day _____ Year _____

City _____

State _____

Country _____

Occupation _____

Date of
Marriage: Month _____ Day _____ Year _____

Place of
Marriage: City _____

State _____

Country _____

_____

_____

_____

_____

Date _____

Place Photo Here

Paternal Great Grandfather

His Full
Name _____

Birth Date: Month ____ Day ____ Year ____

City _____

State _____

Country _____

Occupation _____

_____

_____

_____

_____

_____

_____

Date _____

Place Photo Here

Great Great Grandparents of the Wife

Place Photo Here

*O*ur great great ancestors who were born in Europe lived in nations disturbed by economic inequities and political unrest. Many of them sought new lives and freedom in this country.

In America, vast new lands were added to the Union, including California, Texas and Oregon. Industry flourished in the north and cotton was king in the south. After the tragic Civil War in the 1860s, the nation resumed its march toward its "Manifest Destiny."

If you've found the vital statistics records of some of your great grandparents, they should lead to similar records of your great great grandparents and even your great great great grandparents.

Maternal Great Great Grandmother

*H*er Full Name _____

*B*irth Date: Month _____ Day _____ Year _____

*C*ity _____

*S*tate _____

*C*ountry _____

*O*ccupation _____

Date _____

Maternal Great Great Grandfather

His Full
Name _____

Birth Date: Month _____ Day _____ Year _____

City _____

State _____

Country _____

Occupation _____

Date of
Marriage: Month _____ Day _____ Year _____

Place of
Marriage: City _____

State _____

Country _____

_____

_____

Place Photo Here

Date _____

Paternal
Great Great Grandmother

*Her Full
Name* _____

Birth Date: Month _____ *Day* _____ *Year* _____

City _____

State _____

Country _____

Occupation _____

*Date of
Marriage: Month* _____ *Day* _____ *Year* _____

*Place of
Marriage: City* _____

State _____

Country _____

_____

_____

Date _____

Place Photo Here

Paternal
Great Great Grandfather

His Full
Name _____

Birth Date: Month _____ Day _____ Year _____

City _____

State _____

Country _____

Occupation _____

_____

_____

_____

_____

_____

_____

Date _____

Place Photo Here

Great Great Grandparents of the Husband

Place Photo Here

You are the descendant of eight great great grandfathers and eight great great grandmothers. Probably most of them were born during the second quarter of the 19th century, either in this country or in Europe. It was a time of great migrations from Ireland, Germany, Britain and other nations to the more promising lands of America, Canada and Australia.

Your persistence and ingenuity will be needed to find the vital statistics of some of your great great grandparents, but you will be gratified by your success in a number of instances if your previous research methods have been sound and thorough.

Date _____

Maternal Great Great Grandmother

Her Full
Name _____

Birth Date: Month ____ Day ____ Year ____
City _____
State _____
Country _____
Occupation _____

Maternal Great Great Grandfather

His Full
Name _____

Birth Date: Month _____ Day _____ Year _____

City _____

State _____

Country _____

Occupation _____

Date of
Marriage: Month _____ Day _____ Year _____

Place of
Marriage: City _____

State _____

Country _____

_____
_____
_____
_____
_____
_____
_____
_____
_____
_____
_____
_____

Place Photo Here

Date _____

_____
_____
_____
_____
_____
_____
_____
_____
_____
_____
_____
_____
_____

Paternal
Great Great Grandmother

*H*er Full
Name _____

*B*irth Date: Month _____ Day _____ Year _____

*C*ity _____

*S*tate _____

*C*ountry _____

*O*ccupation _____

Date _____

Place Photo Here

Paternal
Great Great Grandfather

His Full
Name _____

Birth Date: Month _____ Day _____ Year _____

City _____

State _____

Country _____

Occupation _____

Date of
Marriage: Month _____ Day _____ Year _____

Place of
Marriage: City _____

State _____

Country _____

_____

_____

Date _____

Place Photo Here

Great Great Great Grandparents of the Wife

Place Photo Here

When you study your Family Tree Chart, you will see that you share your maiden name with only one of your thirty-two great great great grandparents. You are indeed the product of many bloodlines and many family names. Many ancestor-hunters at first concentrate on tracing the lineage of their surname, and only later realize the full and equal importance of all their other ancestors and ancestresses.

If tracing your forefathers becomes one of your hobbies, you might be surprised at the amount of information you can discover about their children, occupations, travels, military service and even their characters.

Maternal
Great Great Great Grandmother

Her Full
Name _____

Birth Date: Month ____ Day ____ Year ____

City _____

State _____

Country _____

Occupation _____

_____

_____

_____

Date _____

_____

_____

_____

_____

_____

_____

_____

_____

_____

_____

_____

_____

_____

_____

Maternal
Great Great Great Grandfather

His Full
Name _____

Birth Date: Month _____ Day _____ Year _____

City _____

State _____

Country _____

Occupation _____

Date of
Marriage: Month _____ Day _____ Year _____

Place of
Marriage: City _____

State _____

Country _____

Place Photo Here

Date _____

Paternal
Great Great Great Grandmother

Her Full
Name

Birth Date: Month ___ Day ___ Year ___

City

State

Country

Occupation

Date

Place Photo Here

Paternal
Great Great Great Grandfather

His Full
Name _____

Birth Date: Month _____ Day _____ Year _____

City _____

State _____

Country _____

Occupation _____

Date of
Marriage: Month _____ Day _____ Year _____

Place of
Marriage: City _____

State _____

Country _____

Date _____

Place Photo Here

Great Great Great Grandparents of the Husband

Your great great great grandparents were probably born in the early years of the 19th century. If they were native Americans, their fathers might have been veterans of the War for Independence. If they were Europeans, their sires might have fought in the Napoleonic Wars.

When you project the time period of your research and the number of ancestors and ancestresses involved, you will immediately understand the necessity of establishing a workable cross-reference and indexing system for the information which your research will produce. Orderliness is as essential in ancestor-tracing as it is in all types of research.

Maternal
Great Great Great Grandmother

Her Full
Name _____

Birth Date: Month ____ Day ____ Year ____

City _____

State _____

Country _____

Occupation _____

_____

_____

Place Photo Here

Date _____

_____

_____

_____

_____

_____

_____

_____

_____

_____

_____

_____

_____

Maternal
Great Great Great Grandfather

His Full
Name _____

Birth Date: Month ____ Day ____ Year ____

City _____

State _____

Country _____

Occupation _____

Date of
Marriage: Month ____ Day ____ Year ____

Place of
Marriage: City _____

State _____

Country _____

_____
_____
_____
_____
_____
_____
_____
_____
_____
_____
_____
_____
_____
_____

Place Photo Here

Date _____

_____
_____
_____
_____
_____
_____
_____
_____
_____
_____
_____
_____
_____
_____

Paternal
Great Great Great Grandmother

*H*er *Full*
Name _____

Birth Date: Month _____ *Day* _____ *Year* _____
City _____

State _____

Country _____

Occupation _____

_____

_____

_____

_____

_____

_____

_____

_____

_____

Date _____

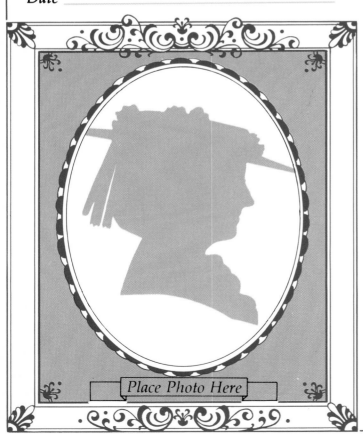

Place Photo Here

Paternal
Great Great Great Grandfather

*His Full
Name* _____

Birth Date: Month _____ *Day* _____ *Year* _____

City _____

State _____

Country _____

Occupation _____

*Date of
Marriage: Month* _____ *Day* _____ *Year* _____

*Place of
Marriage: City* _____

State _____

Country _____

_____

_____

_____

Date _____

Place Photo Here

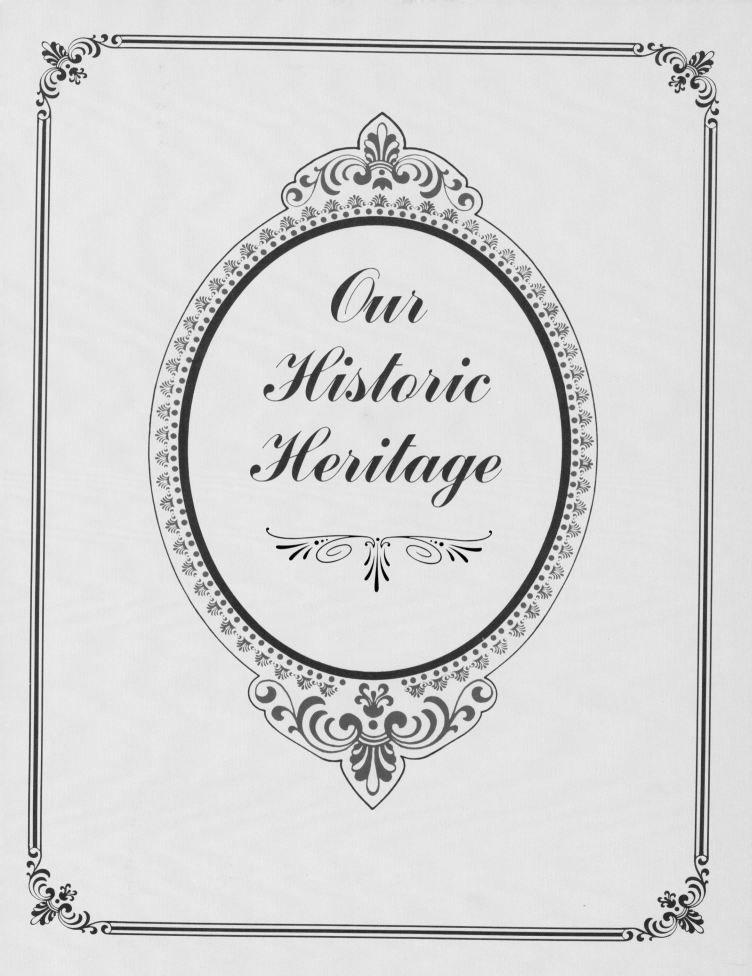

Our Historic Heritage

Husband's Ancestry

Husband's Paternal Grandfather's Full Name - H4

Husband's Paternal Grandmother's Full Name - H5

Date of Marriage   Place of Marriage

Children

Husband's Father's Full Name - H2

Husband's Mother's Full Name - H3

Date of Marriage   Place of Marriage

Children

Husband's Maternal Grandfather's Full Name - H6

Husband's Maternal Grandmother's Full Name - H7

Date of Marriage   Place of Marriage

Children

Wife's Ancestry

Wife's Paternal Grandfather's Full Name - W4

Wife's Paternal Grandmother's Full Name - W5

Date of Marriage   Place of Marriage

Children

Wife's Father's Full Name - W2

Wife's Mother's Full Name - W3

Date of Marriage   Place of Marriage

Children

Wife's Maternal Grandfather's Full Name - W6

Wife's Maternal Grandmother's Full Name - W7

Date of Marriage   Place of Marriage

Children

Our Family Tree

Husband's Full Name - H1 _____

Wife's Full Name - W1 _____

Date of Marriage _____

Place of Marriage _____

Our Children _____

_____

_____

Note: *Each person on this chart is given an identifying code number and letter. You might want to use them as a quick cross-reference system in the various chapters in this book and in your notebooks, work sheets, etc.*

The Husband is H1. His father is H2, and his mother is H3. The Wife is W1, and her father and mother are W2 and W3. As you can see, the other code identifications are a logical extension of this shorthand method.

Wife's Ancestry

Husband's Ancestry

Husband's Great, Great, Great Grandfather's Full Name - H32

H33 - Husband's Great, Great, Great Grandmother's Full Name

Husband's Great, Great, Great Grandfather's Full Name - H34

H35 - Husband's Great, Great, Great Grandmother's Full Name

Husband's Great, Great, Great Grandfather's Full Name - H36

H37 - Husband's Great, Great, Great Grandmother's Full Name

Husband's Great, Great, Great Grandfather's Full Name - H38

H39 - Husband's Great, Great, Great Grandmother's Full Name

Husband's Great, Great, Great Grandfather's Full Name - H40

H41 - Husband's Great, Great, Great Grandmother's Full Name

Husband's Great, Great, Great Grandfather's Full Name - H42

H43 - Husband's Great, Great, Great Grandmother's Full Name

Husband's Great, Great, Great Grandfather's Full Name - H44

H45 - Husband's Great, Great, Great Grandmother's Full Name

Husband's Great, Great, Great Grandfather's Full Name - H46

H47 - Husband's Great, Great, Great Grandmother's Full Name

Husband's Great, Great, Great Grandfather's Full Name - H48

H49 - Husband's Great, Great, Great Grandmother's Full Name

Husband's Great, Great, Great Grandfather's Full Name - H50

H51 - Husband's Great, Great, Great Grandmother's Full Name

Husband's Great, Great, Great Grandfather's Full Name - H52

H53 - Husband's Great, Great, Great Grandmother's Full Name

Husband's Great, Great, Great Grandfather's Full Name - H54

H55 - Husband's Great, Great, Great Grandmother's Full Name

Husband's Great, Great, Great Grandfather's Full Name - H56

H57 - Husband's Great, Great, Great Grandmother's Full Name

Husband's Great, Great, Great Grandfather's Full Name - H58

H59 - Husband's Great, Great, Great Grandmother's Full Name

Husband's Great, Great, Great Grandfather's Full Name - H60

H61 - Husband's Great, Great, Great Grandmother's Full Name

Husband's Great, Great, Great Grandfather's Full Name - H62

H63 - Husband's Great, Great, Great Grandmother's Full Name

Wife's Great, Great, Great Grandfather's Full Name - W32

W33 - Wife's Great, Great, Great Grandmother's Full Name

Wife's Great, Great, Great Grandfather's Full Name - W34

W35 - Wife's Great, Great, Great Grandmother's Full Name

Wife's Great, Great, Great Grandfather's Full Name - W36

W37 - Wife's Great, Great, Great Grandmother's Full Name

Wife's Great, Great, Great Grandfather's Full Name - W38

W37 - Wife's Great, Great, Great Grandmother's Full Name

Wife's Great, Great, Great Grandfather's Full Name - W40

W41 - Wife's Great, Great, Great Grandmother's Full Name

Wife's Great, Great, Great Grandfather's Full Name - W42

W43 - Wife's Great, Great, Great Grandmother's Full Name

Wife's Great, Great, Great Grandfather's Full Name - W44

W45 - Wife's Great, Great, Great Grandmother's Full Name

Wife's Great, Great, Great Grandfather's Full Name - W46

W47 - Wife's Great, Great, Great Grandmother's Full Name

Wife's Great, Great, Great Grandfather's Full Name - W48

W49 - Wife's Great, Great, Great Grandmother's Full Name

Wife's Great, Great, Great Grandfather's Full Name - W50

W51 - Wife's Great, Great, Great Grandmother's Full Name

Wife's Great, Great, Great Grandfather's Full Name - W52

W53 - Wife's Great, Great, Great Grandmother's Full Name

Wife's Great, Great, Great Grandfather's Full Name - W54

W55 - Wife's Great, Great, Great Grandmother's Full Name

Wife's Great, Great, Great Grandfather's Full Name - W56

W57 - Wife's Great, Great, Great Grandmother's Full Name

Wife's Great, Great, Great Grandfather's Full Name - W58

W59 - Wife's Great, Great, Great Grandmother's Full Name

Wife's Great, Great, Great Grandfather's Full Name - W60

W61 - Wife's Great, Great, Great Grandmother's Full Name

Wife's Great, Great, Great Grandfather's Full Name - W62

W63 - Wife's Great, Great, Great Grandmother's Full Name

Husband's Great, Great Grandfather's Full Name - H16

Husband's Great, Great Grandmother's Full Name - H17

Husband's Great Grandfather's Full Name - H8

Husband's Great Grandmother's Full Name - H9

Husband's Great, Great Grandfather's Full Name - H18

Husband's Great, Great Grandmother's Full Name - H19

Husband's Great, Great Grandfather's Full Name - H20

Husband's Great, Great Grandmother's Full Name - H21

Husband's Great Grandfather's Full Name - H10

Husband's Great Grandmother's Full Name - H11

Husband's Great, Great Grandfather's Full Name - H22

Husband's Great, Great Grandmother's Full Name - H23

Husband's Great, Great Grandfather's Full Name - H24

Husband's Great, Great Grandmother's Full Name - H25

Husband's Great Grandfather's Full Name - H12

Husband's Great Grandmother's Full Name - H13

Husband's Great, Great Grandfather's Full Name - H26

Husband's Great, Great Grandmother's Full Name - H27

Husband's Great, Great Grandfather's Full Name - H28

Husband's Great, Great Grandmother's Full Name - H29

Husband's Great Grandfather's Full Name - H14

Husband's Great Grandmother's Full Name - H15

Husband's Great, Great Grandfather's Full Name - H30

Husband's Great, Great Grandmother's Full Name - H31

Wife's Great, Great Grandfather's Full Name - W16

Wife's Great, Great Grandmother's Full Name - W17

Wife's Great Grandfather's Full Name - W8

Wife's Great Grandmother's Full Name - W9

Wife's Great, Great Grandfather's Full Name - W18

Wife's Great, Great Grandmother's Full Name - W19

Wife's Great, Great Grandfather's Full Name - W20

Wife's Great, Great Grandmother's Full Name - W21

Wife's Great Grandfather's Full Name - W10

Wife's Great Grandmother's Full Name - W11

Wife's Great, Great Grandfather's Full Name - W22

Wife's Great, Great Grandmother's Full Name - W23

Wife's Great, Great Grandfather's Full Name - W24

Wife's Great, Great Grandmother's Full Name - W25

Wife's Great Grandfather's Full Name - W12

Wife's Great Grandmother's Full Name - W13

Wife's Great, Great Grandfather's Full Name - W26

Wife's Great, Great Grandmother's Full Name - W27

Wife's Great, Great Grandfather's Full Name - W28

Wife's Great, Great Grandmother's Full Name - W29

Wife's Great Grandfather's Full Name - W14

Wife's Great Grandmother's Full Name - W15

Wife's Great, Great Grandfather's Full Name - W30

Wife's Great, Great Grandmother's Full Name - W31

The Origins of Our Family Names

"We are the children of many sires, and every drop of blood in us reveals our ancestors," wrote philosopher Ralph Waldo Emerson. His penetrating words will take on new meaning when you turn to your Family Tree Chart on page 146. You will see that you are indeed the product of many bloodlines, and you will realize, probably for the first time, that you are also the inheritor of thirty-two different family names from the five generations of your ancestors and ancestresses shown on your Family Tree Chart.

We hope that this chapter will bring you a deeper understanding of the history and significance of your family name and the names of your mother, your ancestors, ancestresses, aunts, uncles and all the other men and women whose names you will record in this Heritage Book.

In these pages, you will learn how our forefathers were given names describing their parentage and occupations, their homes and villages, their appearance and personality, their virtues and religious faith, their courage and strength, their habits and idiosyncrasies.

You will also sense the vital role which a family name played in the lives of our ancestors. For them it was a source of sincere and fervent pride, no matter how humble it might appear. For men and women of all walks of life, their names were symbols which united them in blood and in spirit with their forefathers, and which brought courage and meaning to their lives.

Upholding the honor of their family names was a sustaining motive for dukes and ditch-diggers, swordsmen and swineherders. To have a "good name" was to have a reputation for integrity in one's work and conduct, and to pass on a "good name" was the goal of every man and woman.

This pride in one's family name was succinctly stated by an English nobleman who remarked, "Most of us in the House of Lords have the family names of tradesmen and farmers. And I'll warrant that most of them are as proud of their family names as they are of their titles."

He might also have pointed out that his name, like many other names, underwent considerable changes in form and spelling as the languages of Europe were slowly evolving. Centuries ago the familiar names of Gilbert, Schultz, Ramirez and Carroll were spelled Gisel-beorht, Scultheizzo, Ragin-Mar and O'Caerbhaill. And today surnames continue to be altered and adapted as families move from one country to another. As long as some semblance to the original name is retained so, too, is the memory of its meaning and its significance.

The Names of the Past

In ancient Palestine and Greece, men and women were identified by a single given or personal name like Abraham, Sarah, Moses, Miriam, Pericles, Demosthenes and Xanthippe. Sometimes paternity was indicated as in Joshua ben Nun (ben meaning "son of - ") and Simon Bar Jonah (bar also meaning "son of - "). Obviously, these were not hereditary surnames which could be passed on to their children, nor could descriptive titles like Uriah the Hittite, Alexander the Great, Aristides the Just, Hillel the Babylonia.

ater, the Romans developed a three-name system which consisted of a given name (praenomen), a clan or gens name (nomen) and a family name (cognomen). This orderly practice accurately identified individuals like Gaius Julius Caesar and Marcus Tullius Cicero, but it was misused during Rome's decadent period and was abandoned after the fall of the Empire in the 5th Century.

During the following five centuries, the naming practices in Europe were haphazard, imaginative and often candid. The three royal grandsons of Charlemagne were called Charles the Bald, Charles the Fat and Charles the Simple. Many names were thought-provoking: Edward the Confessor, Ethelred the Unready, Conn of the Hundred Battles, Niall of the Nine Hostages, Leif the Lucky, Brendan the Navigator and William the Bastard who was later known as William the Conqueror. The so-called common people also had their nicknames: Stout Jon, Cedric the Shepherd, Ala the Good, Marya the Baker, Ulf the Stammerer, Memmo the Bear, Marco the Goat, Dark Edda.

he use of hereditary family names developed spontaneously among the Irish in the early 10th century and later among some of the merchant families of Italy. However, the benefits of passing on one's name to one's children were not fully recognized in Europe until the Crusades of the 11th, 12th and 13th centuries. When thousands of men speaking different language

and dialects were banded together, the need for more precise identification became apparent. After the Crusaders departed for the Holy Land, many of them were never heard from again, and others returned only after years of absence. So the wives, sons and daughters of noblemen took the names of their husbands and fathers in order to manage their properties and to inherit their titles and estates.

The people of all classes of society were encouraged to adopt hereditary family names by the priests and officials who kept the church and manorial records. By the 13th and 14th centuries, the practice of passing on one's surname to one's children was widespread in Europe. During these years it also became customary for wives to assume the family names of their husbands.

The Sources of Family Names

Although the people of Europe differed in their racial characteristics and customs, they shared the same religious traditions and they lived within the same feudal system which governed their lives politically, socially and economically.

s a result there were consistent similarities between the surnaming practices among European people whether their languages and racial origins were Latin, Greek, Celtic, Teutonic, Slavic or Hebrew. For the hundreds of basic surnames in each country, there are similar equivalents in the languages of other countries.

To simplify this study of name origins, we have divided them into six classifications:

1. **Occupational Names** were derived from one's occupation, profession, trade or class. A man who ground flour, for instance, was called Miller, Molina, Mo-

linaro, Molyneux and Mueller in England, Spain, Italy, France and Germany.

2. **Patronymic and Matronymic Names** were based on the names of one's father, mother or ancestor. Ivanov, Janowicz, Jantzen, Jensen and McShane are forms of "John's son." Babcock and Babson mean "Son of Bab," a shortened form of Barbara.

3. **Nicknames** described a person's physical characteristics, mannerisms, habits, appearance, virtues, etc. Light-complected or white-haired people were named Bilek in Bohemia, Labno in Poland, Weiss in Germany and White in England.

4. **Animals and Birds** were the source of many surnames. People named Fox were called Fuchs in Germany, Lisiski in Poland, Liska in Bohemia, Renard in France, Volpe in Italy and Voss in Holland.

5. **Geographical Names** indicated one's nationality or place of origin, such as English, Hollander, Bristol, Bressler (a person from Breslau), Lorraine, Romano, Moskowitz, Lincoln, Disraeli.

6. **Homestead and Village Names** were derived from landscape features and man-made structures near one's home or village. People with the names of Hill, Berg, Aguirre, Hough, Haug and Kopecky lived on or near a hill.

Villages of the Middle Ages

In medieval Europe more than 90% of the people lived in small villages, and it was from these rural communities that most of our family names originated. The following description of life in an English manor would generally apply to the thousands of similar villages in the other countries of Europe.

 typical village was located on the estate or manor of a man of noble or gentle birth who lived with his family in a castle or large fortified house set apart from the village itself. Around the single street were clustered the dwellings of the common people who were called freemen (also termed vassals and yeomen) and the more numerous villeins, serfs and cotters.

Occupational Names

Binding together the lords and villagers was a complex system of titles, privileges, duties and exchanges of goods and services. Their occupations and titles were basically the same throughout feudal European society. For example, every village had a blacksmith who fashioned the metal tools and utensils and who sharpened the plowshares and axes. Note the similarity of the names meaning "smith" within each of the basic language groups listed below.

Language Group	Surnames Meaning "Smith"
TEUTONIC	
Danish	Smed
Dutch	Schmidt, Schmitz, Smidt
English	Smith, Smyth, Smythe
Flemish	De Smet, De Smedt
German	Schmidt, Schmitz, Schmitt, Schmid
Norwegian	Smid
Swedish	Smed
LATIN	
French	Le Fevre, Le Febvre, Ferrier, Faure
Italian	Ferraro, Ferrari
Portuguese	Ferreiro
Spanish	Ferrer, Herrara
CELTIC	
Irish	Gowan, Gowen, Gough
Scottish	Gow, Gowan
Welsh	Goff, Gowan
SLAVIC	
Bulgarian	Kovac

Croatian	Kovac
Czech	Kovar, Kovarik, Kovarsky
Estonian	Kalevi
Hungarian	Kovacs, Kovats
Latvian	Kalejs
Lithuanian	Kalvis, Kalvaitis
Polish	Kowal, Kowalsky, Kowalczyk
Romanian	Covaciu
Russian	Koval, Kuznetzov, Kowalsky
Slovak	Kovac

The lord of the manor appointed freemen as officials with specific duties in the management of his household, lands, courts, and in the collection of rents, fees and services from the villagers. In time, their titles were given to them as surnames: Steward (Stewart, Stuart), Bailey (Bayley, Baylie), Reeve (Reeves, Reaves, Reavis), Constable, Sergeant (Sargent) and Beadle (Bedell) who was a court officer.

Other officials were either appointed by the lord or chosen by the freemen. The most important was the Hayward who was responsible for maintaining the fences and hedges which protected the fields. From his title are derived the surnames of Hayward, Hayes, Hays, Haynes or Hayman. The Forester guarded the lord's deer and game, and the Parker was in charge of the lord's park lands. The Woodward or Woodruff supervised the cutting, gathering and distribution of wood.

The Miller ground the villagers' grain which was stored by the Granger. The village's swine were tended by a hog-herder (Hoggart, Hogarth) or swine-herder (Swinehart). There was also a cow-herder (Cowart, Coward, Cowie), calf-herder (Calvert), bull-herder (Bullard), ox-herder (Oxnard), shepherd (Shepherd, Shephard, Sheppard), ewe-herder (Ewart) and a bee-keeper (Beaman, Beeman).

In the larger towns and cities, the artisans, tradesmen and workers were also proud to be named after their crafts and callings. In the cloth-making trades were the Weaver or Weber, Fuller, Tucker, Cutter, Dyer and Walker who treaded or walked on the wool before the invention of rollers. Among the skilled craftsmen were the Taylor, Mercer (silk merchant), Draper, Napier (linen merchant), Shoemaker, Chaucer (also a shoemaker), Glover, Buckler, Goldsmith, and Cutler who made knives and cutting tools. Leather-workers included the Skinner, Tanner and Currier. Popular occupation names were Baker, Butcher, Brewer, Barber, Potter, Cook and Vintner. Chapman, Faraday and Crammer were the names of traveling merchants and peddlers.

In the Middle Ages, women were engaged in many trades and crafts, and if they were single, strong-willed or proficient, they might have been given any of the above surnames. We do know that Baxter, Webster and Brewster are the surnames for women who were bakers, weavers and brewers.

The building trade gave us the names of Mason, Waller, Tyler, Carpenter, Turner (lathe-worker), Joyner, Sawyer, Wright (a woodworker), Carver (a stone carver) and Plumber. Seafarers included Shipman (a captain), Marner, Mariner, Seaman and Boatman. Cartwright and Wheeler supplied the wagons for Carter, Wagner, Waggoner and Waner. Hooper made the iron hoops for Cooper, the maker of barrels and casks.

The entourages of the great nobles also added to the store of surnames. Many of their titles were originally French. The Butler derived his name from the French word for bottle (bouteille), and he was in charge of the wine cellar. The man responsible for managing the lord's household accounts and affairs was the Chamberlain, a title derived from the French word for room (chambre). The Clarke or Clark (clerque) was the scribe or scholar, and the man who dispensed food and provisions was the Spencer or Spenser (despenser).

The man in charge of the lord's horses was

the Marshall, later a title for a high-ranking military officer. The Coulter was entrusted with the breeding and training of young colts. The master of the hunt was called the Hunter or Hunt, and the Falconer or Faulkner was the honored keeper of the lord's hawks. A young boy attending the lord's lady was a Page. He was later called Squire when he was training to become a Knight. The Armour, Fletcher (arrow-maker), Boyer (bow-maker) and Sadler equipped the Bowman, Archer and Spearman in the nobleman's forces.

Patronymics and Matronymics

Surnames derived from one's father or mother are called patronymics and matronymics. They are formed by adding a prefix (meaning "son of - ") or a suffix (meaning " -son") to the father's or mother's name.

atronymics are relatively rare. The wife's name might be adopted if she or her family were wealthy or prominent, or if the husband was off on a long Crusade or voyage. It might also be used if the husband's identity was unknown. Examples of matronymics are Babson (son of Bab or Barbara), Allison (son of Alice), Betts (son of Betty), Agee (son of Alice), Mariott (son of Mary). Jewish surnames often honor outstanding ancestresses, and most of their names beginning with Edel-, Rose- and Blum- venerate a beloved matriarch named Adele, Rosa or Bluma. However, there are so few European matronymics that they are usually included in the inclusive title of patronymics.

In the list below, the patronymical prefixes and suffixes are aligned with the nationalities with which they are frequently associated. Migrations and shifting borders have caused the intermingling of prefixes and suffixes among the neighboring countries and people of Europe.

Nationality or Language	Patronymical Prefix or Suffix
Anglo-Saxon	-ing
Armenian	-ian
Bulgarian	-off, -eff
Czechoslovakian	-an, -ak, -ek, -ic, -ov, -ko, -icz -ova (daughter of)
Danish	-sen
Dutch	-en, -zen, -z
English	-son, -s
Finnish	-nin
French	de-, d'-
German	-sohn, -zohn, -s, -z
Greek	-opoulos, -antis
Hebrew	bar, ben
Hungarian	-f, -fi
Irish	Mac-, Mc- O'- (grandson of)
Italian	de-, di-, d'-, degli
Lithuanian	-aites, -as, -is
Norman	Fitz-
Norwegian	-sen, -son -datter (daughter of)
Polish	-wicz, -ski, -zki, -cki -ska (daughter of)
Portuguese	-es, -az
Romanian	-escu
Russian	-itch, -ich, -vich, -ov, -of, -off, -ef, -eff -ev, -if, -enak, -enko -ovna (daughter of)
Scottish	Mac-
Spanish	-es, -ez
Swedish	-son
Welsh	-s -Ab-, Ap-, Up-
Yugoslavian	-ak, -ek, -ic

Patronymic Surname	Meaning of Surname
Denning	Son of Dene
Bedrosian	Son of Peter
Georgieff	Son of George
Matusek	Son of Matthew
Petrova	Daughter of Peter
Jansen	Son of John
Jantzen	Son of John
Robertson	Son of Robert
Heikkinen	Son of Henry
De Nys	Son of Denys
Heinsohn	Son of Hein
Angelopoulos	Son of Angelo
ben Gurion	Son of Gurion
Mihaly	Son of Michael
McCormick	Son of Cormack
O'Neill	Grandson of Niall
De Luca	Son of Luke
Petrauskas	Son of Peter
Fitzsimmons	Son of Simon
Monsen	Son of Magnus
Halvordatter	Daughter of Halvor
Adamowicz	Son of Adam
Sklodowska	Daughter of Sklodowski
Gomes	Son of Gumersindo
Antonescu	Son of Anthony
Ivanov	Son of Ivan
Ivanovna	Daughter of Ivan
MacGregor	Son of Gregory
Hernandez	Son of Hernando
Svenson	Son of Sven
Davis	Son of David
Bevan	Son of Evan (Ab Evan)
Jovanovich	Son of John

nvasions and population movements greatly influenced the selection of given names and patronyms throughout Europe. For instance, when the Normans conquered England, they brought with them a new supply of given or Christian names: William, Robert, Roger, Hugh, Ralph, Walter, Geoffrey, Baldwin, Richard, Henry, Gerald, Gerard and a few others. These names were of Frankish or Teutonic origin, and some of them were dithematic in form. Dithematic describes a name composed of two root words which have no apparent connection with one another. Ralph was derived from Raed-wulf, meaning "counselor; wolf," and William was originally Will-helm meaning "resolution; helmet." The Normans also favored apostles' names, particularly John, Thomas, Peter, Philip and Simon.

Within a generation or two, the Norman names had supplanted the old Anglo-Saxon names (Alfred, Edgar, Edward, Aethelstane, Cedric, etc.) among the upper classes, and they spread into the small villages where they became so common that half of a small hamlet's male population might answer to the three names of William, Robert and John.

This would have caused complete confusion but for the widespread use of "pet names," a term describing a shortened and affectionate form of a given name.

For example, a few of the pet names for Robert were Rob, Robbie, Robin, Hob and Dob. From the single name of Robert and its pet names were derived the following hereditary surnames: Robert, Robertson, Robb, Robbins, Robbinson, Robinson, Robins, Robeson, Robbie, Robey, Robson, Hobbs, Hobbins, Hobinson, Hobson, Dobson, Dobbie, Dobey, Doble, etc. There were almost as many pet names (and subsequent hereditary surnames) for William, Henry, Richard and the other Norman names. All the peoples of Europe followed this practice of shortening their baptismal names into pet names and then incorporating them into surnames.

Often pet names were modified affectionately by suffixes called diminutives which indicated the youth or small size of the name-bearer. Sometimes a pet name with its diminutive became a surname. The name Watkins, for instance, is derived from Wat, a pet name for Walter, plus the diminutive -kins. Similarly, Heinlein is formed from Hein, a pet name for Heinrich, with the diminutive -lein. Marchetti is a pet form of Marco, plus the diminutive -etti, and Michelin is a pet form of Michele with the diminutive -lin.

Diminutive endings were most frequently used in patronymics by the English, French, Germans and Italians.

Languages	Diminutive Suffixes
English	-cock, -et, -ie, -in, -kin, -kins, -on, -y
French	-eau, -el, -elin, -elet, -elle, -et, -ette, -let, -lin, -net, -on, -ot, -otte
German	-chen, -el, -ich, -ig, -ke, -kel, -ken, -le, -lein, -len, -licke, -lin, -zel, -zke
Italian	-cello, -cino, -ello, -etto, -ino, -itto, -occo, -ucco

Descriptive Nicknames

The people of the Middle Ages loved nicknames, and they used them freely to describe one another's appearance, habits, character and disposition. They give a fascinating insight into the lives and attitudes of our ancestors: their respect for courage, strength and integrity, their deep religious faith, their playfulness, frankness, compassion and cruelty.

nly a nickname which was especially appropriate for an individual was given to him as a surname. The man named Blanchard (meaning "blond, strong"), must have been the most powerful fair-haired man in his village. To be given the name Long (meaning "tall"), a man had to tower above his fellows.

Among the nicknames (and later surnames) for tall men were Lange or Lang in Germany, Grande in France, Longo in Italy, Nagy in Hungary and Groot in Holland. A small man might be called Little or Small in England, Klein or Kurtz in Germany, Le Cour in France, Basso in Italy, Kiss in Hungary, Niziolek in Poland, Malenkov in Russia.

Corpulence was often considered a status symbol of the well-to-do, so names such as Legros, Grassi, Grossman and Grant were esteemed in France, Italy, Germany and England.

Light-haired and light-complected people were called Blount (blond) in England, Weiss in Germany, Finn and Gaynor in Ireland, Bianco in Italy, Labno in Poland, Bilek in Czechoslovakia, Le Blanc in France, Baines in Scotland, Gwynn or Wynn in Wales.

Red-haired men were given the names of Roth in Germany, Reed and Russell in England, Rousseau and Roux in France, Pyrrhos in Greece, Voros in Hungary, Flynn and Flannery in Ireland, Rossini and Rossa in Italy, Rudzinski in Poland, Cerney in Czechoslovakia.

People with very dark hair or swarthy complexions were named Brown, Moore and Black in England, Braun and Schwartz in Germany, Donnegan and Dunne in Ireland, Chernoff in Russia, Moreno and Mauro in Italy, Czernok in Poland, Cerny in Czechoslovakia, Moro in Spain, Moreau in France.

Men who were outstandingly handsome were named Schoen in Germany, Beauregard and Le Beau in France, Cavanaugh and Kiley in Ireland, and Jaffe among Jews.

The above nicknames described the physical appearance of individuals, while others highlighted their character or disposition. Men who were loved for their kindness and courtesy were called Doucette in France,

Zeiss in Germany, *O'Keefe* in Ireland, *Gentile* and *Graziano* in Italy, *Curtis* and *Bonham* in England. Those who had displayed great bravery in battle were named *Farrell* and *Connelly* by the Irish, *Doughty* and *Stout* by the English, *Wyethe* by the Welsh, *Valente* by the Italians, *Vaillant* by the French and *Kreiger* by the Germans.

In Germany, a man noted for his piety was given the name of *Gottschalk* or "Servant of God." *Guzman* in Spain and *L'Hommedieu* in France meant "Man of God." Irishmen who were devoted to particular saints were called *Mulvihill* (Follower of St. Michael) and *Gilbride* (Servant of St. Bridget).

Warm-hearted and amiable men were known as *Goodfellow*, *Bonner* and *Goodheart* in England, *Bono* and *Bonelli* in Italy, *Bonamy* in France. A man who punctuated his remarks with "Par Dieu!" ("By God!") was called *Pardieu*, *Pardee* and *Purdue*. One who cheerfully wished everyone "Good day" was named *Gooday* in England, *Guttendag* in Germany, *Bongiorno* in Italy.

By our standards, our ancestors were often crude and cruel when giving names to their fellows. However, these names reflect the frank and outspoken spirit of their times, and the men who received them were as proud of them as King Charles the Fat and King William the Bastard. For the Scots of the Middle Ages, it was natural and proper to call a man *Campbell* if he had a twisted mouth and to give the name of *Cameron* to a hook-nosed man. In Germany, a person with a "nose like a crane" was casually given the name of *Kronschnabel*. In Italy, the original *Caputo* had an oversized head while *Capozzo's* head was abnormally small. Men who were crippled or lame were named *Cruickshank* in Scotland, *Kryvenko* in Russia, *Crockett* in England. *Calvin*, *Mullins* and *Pollard* either shaved their heads or were quite bald. In Spain, the name *Aparicio* was given to a man who was as emaciated as a ghost or apparition.

In Germany, *Brummer* was a grumbler, and *Klotz* was clumsy and awkward. Men who

were lazy and sleepy were called *Klimala* in Bohemia. Those who were quarrelsome were named *Kreiter* in Germany, *Connors* in Ireland and *Baratta* in Italy.

All nicknames are not what they seem. Men who drank water and abstained from wine were called *Bevilaqua* in Italy and *Boileau* in France. In some cases, these names might have been tongue-in-cheek jibes at men who overindulged in alcoholic beverages. It would seem that active, energetic men were called *Mussolini* (little gnat) in Italy, *Fleigel* (fly) in Germany, *Bonk* (horsefly) in Poland, *Krushchev* and *Zhukov* (beetles) in Russia. It is just as likely they had the irritating characteristics of their insect namesakes. And *Krushchev* and *Zhukov* might have been named after the lucky scarabs which they carried. Although the names *Powers* and *Power* in Ireland meant "a poor man," they described highly-respected men who had willingly taken a vow of poverty for religious reasons. *Belcher* seems to be a nickname for a man with unpleasant habits, but it is derived from the French "bel-cher" and means "the beautiful, beloved one."

Names Derived from Animals and Birds

There are four original sources for surnames in this category:

> Animalistic family totems
> Animal-human resemblances
> Heraldic animals of noblemen
> Trades and shop signboards

 s we explain these four sources, you will understand why it is sometimes difficult to positively assign a surname to its original source. For instance, a man might have been named *Bear* because (1) it was the totem animal of his family or clan, (2) he possessed bearlike strength, (3) as a

soldier, he wore his lord's heraldic bear on his surcoat, (4) he painted a bear on his shop's signboard.

The belief in supernatural totem animals probably began in prehistoric times when man first became a hunter. He was awed by the powerful bears and fearless boars, the relentless wolves and the fleet horses, the soaring eagles and hawks. Clearly they were superior to him in many ways, so he endowed them with human emotions and godlike powers.

Out of this fascination grew legends about totem animals and birds which abound in European folklore. People believed that these godlike creatures chose favored men and women for whom they performed miraculous deeds. In some cases, the animal-gods fell in love with human beings, and these unions produced heroes and heroines with supernatural powers. The tale of Romulus and Remus being adopted by a she-wolf is a later version of the original myth that she was their actual mother. Hengist and Horsa, the Jute Kings who invaded England, were believed to have been fathered by a horse-god.

Many of the great chiefs and warriors claimed descent from animal-gods and bird-gods, and they adopted their names as their own. The memory of these totem creatures are retained in some names by identifying root words: **arn-** (eagle) **leo-, len-, loew-** (lion), **eber-, ever-, aver-** (boar), **loup, lup-, ulf-, wulf, vol-** (wolf), **ber-, bern-, bjorn-** (bear). If you have one of these root syllables in your name, it's possible that it was derived from a totem animal. However, it's far more probable that it came from one of the three following sources.

One of these sources of surnames was the human inclination to find imaginative resemblances between some people and specific animals and birds. We still make these comparisons today when we say that a powerful man is a bull, that a dandified fellow is a peacock, that a diligent worker is a beaver. In the Middle Ages, these men would probably have been given the names

of Bull, Peacock and Beaver. In similar fashion, a man who was both intelligent and strong might be named Bear in England, Baer or Behrens in Germany, McMahon in Ireland and Urso in Italy. A renowned warrior would be called Wolf or Wolfe in England, Wulff in Germany, Lopez in Spain, Lupo in Italy, Lupowitz in Poland, Lykos in Greece, Lupescu in Romania, Volkov in Russia.

Animal nicknames (later surnames) were varied and imaginative. Men named Parrott and Jay probably talked incessantly. Men called Fox, Foxe, Foxx and Todd were red-haired or very clever. A long-legged person might have been called Crane or Heron. Peace-loving men would be called Dove or Lamb. Swan must have been both handsome and graceful, and Sparrow probably hopped about energetically.

Often animals and birds were symbols on a nobleman's coat of arms or helmet crest, and these identifying emblems were often sewn on the surcoats of his soldiers. The lord's retainers and servants also wore his emblem on their clothing. They were proud of these symbols of their status and sometimes chose them as their surnames.

Other surnames were derived from a person's trade. Men named Fowler, Finch and Partridge caught and sold birds. Those named Fish, Fisher, Pike, Shattuck (shad) and Trout caught and sold fish. Hogg and Bacon sold pork, lard and bacon. If these people had shops, they probably pictured the appropriate animal, bird or fish on a signboard over the door.

This introduces the subject of signboards, which were a popular source of animal surnames. Since very few people were able to read, most shops and taverns used painted signboards to identify themselves or their trade. Some pictured an object such as a Bell (for a tavern) or a Bush (for a wine-merchant), while others depicted almost every animal, bird and fish known in medieval Europe.

There were a variety of reasons why a man painted a specific animal or bird on the signboard which identified his shop, tavern or house. It might have depicted his descriptive surname, his nickname, his trade, his lord's heraldic symbol, or he might just have been fond of that particular creature. It often followed that the families who owned and lived in these shops were named after the creature on their signboards: Badger, Bear, Bird, Byrd, Boar, Bull, Bullock, Cock, Crane, Crow, Dove, Drake, Finch, Fox, Hare, Hart, Hawke, Heron, Jay, Kidd, Lamb, Lyon, Parrott, Partridge, Peacock, Pidgeon, Pike, Raven, Stagg, Swan, Trout, Wren, Wolf, etc.

Many of the signs on the shops and houses owned by Jewish families held deep significance for them. During the centuries when they were forbidden to have Jewish names or to profess their heritage in any way, they used their signboards to circumvent these laws. In Germany, some Jews of the Israelite tribe of Judah painted the symbolic lion on their signboards, and then took the name of Loew, Loewy or Loeb (all of them meaning "lion"). Members of the tribe of Benjamin would have a wolf on their signboards and take the name of Wulf, Wulff, Wolfenberg, etc. A deer or hart on a signboard represented the tribe of Naphtali, and the family was called Hartz, Hertz, Herz, Hersch, Hirsch or Hirschman. An ox symbolized the people of Ephraim, and they took the name of Ochs.

Geographical Names

Individuals and families from all classes of medieval society adopted the names of the countries, provinces, counties and cities of their origins.

embers of the royalty and higher nobility took as titles the names of the countries and provinces which they ruled, while people of the lesser nobility and gentle blood were named after their castles and estates. This relation was indicated by the preposition "of" in England, "de" in France, Italy, Spain and Portugal, "von"

in Germany and Austria, and by the suffix "sky" in Poland and Russia, and "-y" in Hungary.

Many prominent men and women were identified by the places of their birth or residence when their reputation and influence spread beyond their communities. Usually they were churchmen, merchants, scholars, artists and artisans. Among them were Thomas of Canterbury, Isaac of York, Duns Scotus (Duns the Irishman), Thomas à Kempis, Joan of Arc, Leonardo da Vinci and Teresa of Avilla.

Far more numerous than these people of noble birth and fame were the thousands of our ancestors who were given the names of their birthplaces when they moved to another town or country. It was natural for the natives to identify newcomers by the places of their origin: Moskowsky (a person from Moscow), Fleming (a man from Flanders), Franco (a Frank or Frenchman in Italy or Spain), Deutsch (a man from Germany).

The following random list illustrates the variety of our geographic and nationality names: Avila, Bayer (a Bavarian), Boehm (a Bohemian), Bressler (a person from Breslau), Bristol, Cornwallis, England, Englander, English, Florsheim, Frankfurter, French, Genovese (a person from Genoa), Greco (a Greek in Spain), Guttenberg, Horvath (a Croatian), Ireland, Irish, Kent, Lincoln, London, Milano, Moynahan (a man from Munster), Osmanski (a man from Turkey), Polakoff (a man from Poland), Romano, Schwab (a Swabian), Slezak (a Silesian), Unger (Hungarian), Washawsky (a person from Warsaw).

When the Norman knights conquered England and Ireland, their names were those of their estates and towns in France. In time these names were slowly changed to their present form by the native Anglo-Saxon and Irish people: d'Arci (Darcy), d'Aubyn (Tobin), de Barri (Barry), de Bohon (Boone), de Burca (Burke), de Courtenai (Courtney), de Cussac (Cussack), d'Evreux (Devereaux), d'Isigny (Disney), de Lassy

(Lacy, De Lacy), de Nogent (Nugent), de Perci (Percy), St. Clair (Sinclair).

Similar adaptations and assimilations took place in Europe following the conquests and migrations of the Middle Ages. It seems that the names and the language of both the invader and the invaded underwent simultaneous interchanges in form and in spelling.

Homestead and Village Names

In the early history of Europe, there were no numbering systems to identify homes, so they were given names which described either their appearance, nearby features of the landscape or their ownership. It followed quite naturally that many families were named after the homes. These names are sometimes called "place names" or "location names."

or instance, let's assume that there was a white stone homestead located in a meadow near a woods. It was owned by a man named Bos. His neighbors might call the homestead either Whiston (meaning "white stone"), or Woodley (**ley** meaning "meadow") or Bosworth (**worth** meaning "homestead"). Bos and his family might be called the people from Whiston, Woodley or Bosworth which would eventually become the family name. If a village grew up around the homestead, it might also be given the same name.

Thousands of families and villages in Europe derived their names in this fashion. Our explanation will center on English place names whose origins generally parallel those of other European countries.

Many names were compound words which included a descriptive or terminating word which was Anglo-Saxon or Danish in origin. Some meanings differed from one locality to another, and they often changed through the centuries. The word **-tun** or

-ton originally meant enclosure, then homestead (farm) and later a manor or town. The endings **-by, -ham,- thorpe, -wick** and **-worth** meant homestead or farm. A fortified place was indicated by **-berg, -burgh, -bury** or **-by.**

The terminations **-leigh, -lee, -lea** and **-ley** meant a wood, then a clearing and finally a meadow. The meanings of **-hill, -field, -grove, -wood** and **-bridge** are clear. Among the other endings are **-hurst** (a wood or hillock), **-shaw** (a small wood), **-down** (hill), **-ey** (island), **-com, -comb** and **-combe** (valley), **-den** (a hill or valley, depending on the locality), **-burn** (a stream), **-well** (a spring or well), **-croft** (an enclosure or field), **-cott** (cottage). The syllable **ing** conveyed the idea of a clan or group of people.

Among the prefixes are **Atte-** and **At-** (meaning near or at), **Old-, Ol-, Al-** (old), **New-,** and the compass points **Nor-, Nort-** (North), **Su- (**South), **Eas-** (East), **Wes-** (West).

Following is a crosssection of place and homestead surnames: Fenton (a homestead near a fen or marsh), Oglethorpe (Okdell's farm), Gresham (a grazing farm or field), Willoughby (a homestead in or near the willows), Pillsbury (Pil's fort), Buckley (a meadow frequented by buck deer), Langdon (a homestead near the long hill or valley), Canfield (Cana's field), Harwood (a wood frequented by hares), Whitney (white island), Lipscomb (at the edge of the valley), Hayden (hay valley), Swinburne (stream where the swine were watered), Caldwell (a cold spring or well), Milford (a mill near the river crossing), Olcott (old cottage), Prescott (the priest's cottage), Crawford (a river crossing frequented by crows), Attebury (a homestead near or at the fortified place), Sutton (a homestead to the south of the village).

Many of the surnames derived from landscape features, boundary markers and buildings have come down to us without prefixes or suffixes: Banks, Barnes, Beck (a small stream), Birch, Bridges, Brooks,

Burns (also a brook), Craig (a boundary marker), Cross (a wayside cross), Dale, Dean (a small valley), Dykes, Fields, Ford, Forest, Green (a village green), Grove, Hall, Heath, Hedges, Hill, Holt and Hurst (a small wood), Lake, Lee, Leigh, Marsh, Meadows, Mills, Oakes, Pine, Pond, Poole, Rivers, Stone (a boundary marker), Street (a Roman road), Travers and Travis (a crossroads), Wall (usually a Roman wall), Wells, Woods.

In their original form, most of the above names had suffixes, prefixes or phrases indicating their relationship (of, in, on or near) to a home or village. The -s endings of some names (Mills, Wells, etc.) did not always indicate plural nouns. Apparently the "s" was added for phonetic affect.

Some of the most beautiful location surnames described features of landscape which are more imaginary than real. In the late 18th century, the rulers of central Europe ordered their Jewish citizens to adopt hereditary surnames which did not indicate their religious faith or heritage. Some of the ghetto-dwelling families selected or created names expressing their hunger for the beauty of nature: Lilienthal (lily valley), Rosenwald (rose forest), Blumberg (flower mountain), Strauss (bouquet of flowers).

One hundred years later the Swedish government was concerned by the overwhelming numbers of families with patronymic names ending in "-son." Thousands of families responded by creating names reflecting their love of poetic imagery and sonorous sound combinations. Some of them have the affect of a still-life picture or a landscape painting: Almgren (elm branch), Lindquist (linden tree twig), Dahlberg (valley mountain), Hedlund (heath grove), Holmstrom (river island stream).

Our Changing Names

As our languages evolved, so too did the spelling of our names. The honored and ancient names of Hruod-beraht, Hwaesyngtun and O'Flaithbeartaigh are scarcely rec-

ognizable in the modern names of Robert, Washington and Flaherty.

It has always been difficult to adapt the sounds of the Anglo-Saxon, Germanic Celtic and Slavic languages to the Latin alphabet, so people have had trouble in writing their names phonetically. Even Shakespeare spelled his own name in five different ways in the five examples of his signature which have come down to us.

One would think that the surname Bunker referred to a military fortification. However, it was originally spelled Boncoeur and it meant that its first bearer was a man of "good heart." The gentle and tender name of Love was spelled Loupe or Loup, meaning "wolf." It was a warrior name given to a savage fighter, or to a man who was believed to be descended from a totem wolf.

These changes were made gradually within the borders of a country. Alterations in form and spelling were more abrupt when families moved from one country or locality to another. During the recent history of immigrations to this country, the names of newcomers of all nationalities were often misspelled or shortened by immigration clerks, civil officials and employers. Aldridge became Aldrich; Diederich was recorded as Dedrick; Armato was misspelled Amato. And the new arrivals could do little to correct the mistake.

Some families also chose to alter their names in order to conform to the pronunciation and spelling patterns of their new homeland. Reggenfelder ("rye field" in Dutch) became Rockefeller, and Pfoershing ("peach tree" in German) was fortunately changed to Pershing. Usually altered names retained the spirit of the original names either in appearance or sound or meaning. The first letter or syllable was retained, or the new name was a translation of the old. For instance, the name Schlittler (meaning "a man who drives a cart") might take the name of Carter.

The Meanings of Our Family Names

ou'll find the definitions and origins of almost 3000 surnames in the preceding chapter and in the **Dictionary of Family Names** which follows. They were selected from the names which appear in the greatest numbers among the 2,000,000 names in our telephone directories and Social Security lists.

As we've pointed out in **The Origins of Our Family Names,** our surnames have meanings which are more significant than their literal translations might indicate. It should be remembered that a surname was given to an individual or family to clearly distinguish them from everyone else in their community. The name Smith was the honored title of the best craftsman in his village. A man called Long (meaning "tall") must have towered above his fellows, and Connelly (meaning "valorous") must have been the most courageous of warriors. The name Beck (meaning "brook") described "**the** person or family whose homestead was near the brook." There were no other Becks in the community.

The definitions in the Dictionary follow this simple form:

Griffin, Griffen (Welsh, Irish). A person who lived at the signboard of the griffin (an heraldic half-lion, half-eagle creature); a person with a ruddy face or red hair.

Explanation: the names Griffin and Griffen are associated with the Welsh and Irish people. There are two alternative meanings which are separated by a semicolon. Alternate meanings are indicated when there is doubt as to the original meaning of a root word, or when a root word has more than one meaning. Most authorities in this field are in general agreement on the definitions in the following dictionary of surnames.

bbott (English). A layman employed by an abbey; one who played the part of an abbot in church pageants; a man with a priestly manner.

Abernathy (Scottish). A person whose homestead was located at the mouth of the clear river.

Abraham, Abrahams, Abrahamson (English, Jewish). Son of Abraham, meaning "father of a multitude."

Abramovich, Abramovitz, Abramowitz (Russian, Yugoslav, Polish, Jewish). Son of Abram, meaning "high father."

Abbruzzo, Abbruzzi (Italian). A person from the region of Abbruzzi.

Acheson (English). Son of Ache, meaning "the swordsman."

Ackerman, Akermann (German, Austrian, English). A plowman or farmer.

Acosta (Spanish). A person from the town of Acosta, meaning "on the seacoast."

Adair (Scottish, Irish). A variant of Edgar, meaning "rich spear;" a person living near the oak-tree ford, from the Gaelic Athdara.

Adamek, Adamik, Adamic (Czechoslovak, Polish). See **Adams.**

Adamoski, Adamowski (Polish). A person from Adamowo or Adam's village.

Adams, Adamson, Addams, Adam (English, Welsh). Son of Adam, meaning "man created from the red earth."

Addison, Adkins, Adkinson (English, Scottish, Welsh). Son of Adam, meaning "man created from the red earth."

Adduci, Adducci (Italian). See **Adams.**

Adler (German, Jewish). The noble warrior; a person whose shop sign pictured an eagle.

164

Agassiz, Agassie (Swiss). A person whose shop sign depicted a magpie.

Agnew (English). A person whose shop sign pictured a lamb; a person with an innocent or lamblike disposition.

Agostino, Agostini (Italian). Son of Augustine, meaning "venerable, majestic." Possibly a person born in August.

Aguilar, Aguilera (Spanish). A person from Aguilas, meaning "the place of eagles."

Aguirre (Spanish). A person from Aguirre, meaning "the high place" or "the place of war."

Ahern, Ahearn, Aherne (Irish). Descendant of Eachthighearna, meaning "the lord of the horses."

Ahlgren (Swedish). Alder branch.

Ahrens (Dutch, Jewish). A person who lived at the signboard of the eagle.

Albert, Alberts, Albertson (English). Descendant of Albert, meaning "the noble, illustrious one."

Albrecht (German, Austrian). Son of Albrecht, meaning "the noble, illustrious one."

Alcazar (Spanish). A person from Alcazar, meaning "the castle."

Alcott (English). A person who lived in the old cottage.

Alden, Aldine, Aldin (English). Descendant of Ealdwine, meaning "old true friend."

Aldrich (English). A form of Alderich, the "old ruler."

Aldridge (English). A family who lived in a village near the alder trees.

Alexander (Scottish, English). Descendant of Alexander, meaning "protector of men."

Allegretti (Italian). A pleasant, happy person.

Allen, Allan, Allyn (English, Scottish). Origin is obscure. Possible meanings include "fierce one;" "green plain;" "cheerful."

Allison, Alison (English, Scottish). Son of Alis, a pet form of Alexander, meaning "protector of men;" a son of Alice, meaning "noble and kind."

Almeda (Spanish). A person from Almeda, meaning "gum tree."

Altgeld, Altgelt (German, Austrian). A man who dealt in old gold.

Altman (German, Austrian). The old, faithful servant.

Altschuler, Altshuler (German, Austrian, Czechoslovak, Jewish). A person who came from the old school; an old and respected schoolteacher; a member of the Old Synagogue of Prague.

Alvarado, Alvara (Spanish). A person who lived near a stone wall or boundary marker; a person from Albarado, meaning "a white place."

Alvarez, Alvaroz (Spanish). A brilliant person; a person with white or light hair.

Amato (Italian). Descendant of Amato, meaning "the beloved one."

Ames (English). Son of Ame, meaning "friend."

Amundsen, Amundson (Norwegian). Son of Aimund, meaning "ancestral protector."

Anderson, Andersen, Anders (English, Swedish, Norwegian, Danish). See *Andrews*.

Andrews, Andrew (Scottish, English). Son of Andrew, meaning "the manly one."

Anselmo (Spanish, Portuguese, Italian). A form of Anselm, meaning "divine helmet" or "divine protection."

Anthony, Antonson, Antonsen, Anton, Antonelli (English, Swedish, Danish, Norwegian, German, Italian). Son of Anthony, meaning "the peerless one."

Antonovich, Antonopoulos, Antonescu (Yugoslav, Russian, Greek, Romanian). See *Anthony*.

Archambault, Archambeau (French, Belgian). Descendant of Aircanbald, meaning "noble and bold."

Archer (English). A warrior armed with bow and arrows.

Arends, Arendt, Arenson, Arenz, Aren (German, Dutch, Norwegian, Danish). Son

Adler (German, Jewish). The noble warrior; a person whose shop sign pictured an eagle.

Agassiz, Agassie (Swiss). A person whose shop sign depicted a magpie.

Agnew (English). A person whose shop sign pictured a lamb; a person with an innocent or lamblike disposition.

Agostino, Agostini (Italian). Son of Augustine, meaning "venerable, majestic." Possibly a person born in August.

Aguilar, Aguilera (Spanish). A person from Aguilas, meaning "the place of eagles."

Aguirre (Spanish). A person from Aguirre, meaning "the high place" or "the place of war."

Ahern, Ahearn, Aherne (Irish). Descendant of Eachthighearna, meaning "the lord of the horses."

Ahlgren (Swedish). Alder branch.

Ahrens (Dutch, Jewish). A person who lived at the signboard of the eagle.

Albert, Alberts, Albertson (English). Descendant of Albert, meaning "the noble, illustrious one."

Albrecht (German, Austrian). Son of Albrecht, meaning "the noble, illustrious one."

Alcazar (Spanish). A person from Alcazar, meaning "the castle."

Alcott (English). A person who lived in the old cottage.

Alden, Aldine, Aldin (English). Descendant of Ealdwine, meaning "old true friend."

Aldrich (English). A form of Alderich, the "old ruler."

Aldridge (English). A family who lived in a village near the alder trees.

Alexander (Scottish, English). Descendant of Alexander, meaning "protector of men."

Allegretti (Italian). A pleasant, happy person.

Allen, Allan, Allyn (English, Scottish). Origin is obscure. Possible meanings include "fierce one;" "green plain;" "cheerful."

Allison, Alison (English, Scottish). Son of Alis, a pet form of Alexander, meaning "protector of men;" a son of Alice, meaning "noble and kind."

Almeda (Spanish). A person from Almeda, meaning "gum tree."

Altgeld, Altgelt (German, Austrian). A man who dealt in old gold.

Altman (German, Austrian). The old, faithful servant.

Altschuler, Altshuler (German, Austrian, Czechoslovak, Jewish). A person who came from the old school; an old and respected schoolteacher; a member of the Old Synagogue of Prague.

Alvarado, Alvara (Spanish). A person who lived near a stone wall or boundary marker; a person from Albarado, meaning "a white place."

Alvarez, Alvaroz (Spanish). A brilliant person; a person with white or light hair.

Amato (Italian). Descendant of Amato, meaning "the beloved one."

Ames (English). Son of Ame, meaning "friend."

Amundsen, Amundson (Norwegian). Son of Aimund, meaning "ancestral protector."

Anderson, Andersen, Anders (English, Swedish, Norwegian, Danish). See **Andrews.**

Andrews, Andrew (Scottish, English). Son of Andrew, meaning "the manly one."

Anselmo (Spanish, Portuguese, Italian). A form of Anselm, meaning "divine helmet" or "divine protection."

Anthony, Antonson, Antonsen, Anton, Antonelli (English, Swedish, Danish, Norwegian, German, Italian). Son of Anthony, meaning "the peerless one."

Antonovich, Antonopoulos, Antonescu (Yugoslav, Russian, Greek, Romanian). See **Anthony.**

Archambault, Archambeau (French, Belgian). Descendant of Aircanbald, meaning "noble and bold."

Archer (English). A warrior armed with bow and arrows.

Arends, Arendt, Arenson, Arenz, Aren

(German, Dutch, Norwegian, Danish). Son of Arend, meaning "the eagle ruler."

Armand, Arman (French, Belgian, Dutch). An army man or a strong man.

Armbruster, Armbrust (German, Dutch, Austrian). A crossbowman or a man who made crossbows.

Armour, Armor (English, Scottish). An armor maker.

Armstrong (English, Scottish). A man with strong arms.

Arnold, Arnolde (English). Descendant of Arnold, meaning "the eagle ruler" or "a place frequented by eagles."

Arnstein (German, Austrian, Jewish). A person from the town of Arnstein, meaning "stony waterway."

Arroyo (Spanish). A person who lived near the small stream.

Arthur (English, Welsh). The origin of Arthur is obscure. Possible meanings: "Thor's eagle;" "brave, noble."

Ascher, Asher, Asch (German, Austrian, Jewish). A person who lived near an ash tree (probably a boundary marker); a person from the town of Asch; a descendant of Ascher, meaning "blessed."

Ashley (English). A person who lived near the meadow by the ash trees.

Astor (English). A person born during Eastertide.

Atchison (Scottish, English). Son of Adkin, a pet form of Adam, meaning "man created from the red earth;" son of Ache, meaning "the swordsman."

Atkins, Atkinson (English, Scottish, Welsh). Son of Addie, a pet form of Adam, meaning "man created from the red earth."

Atwater, Attwater (English). A person who lived near a pond or stream.

Atwood (English). A person whose homestead was near the wood.

Auslander (German, Austrian). A man who came from another country, a foreigner.

Austin, Austen (English, Scottish). Forms of Augustine, which means "venerable, majestic."

Averill (English). A person who lived at the hill of the wild boar.

Avery (English). Son of Everhard, meaning "strong boar."

Avila (Spanish, Portuguese). A person from the town of Avila, meaning "a place which has been liberated."

Axelrod, Axelrood (English). A dweller in the clearing among the ash trees.

Ayers, Ayer (English). A son of the heir to property.

Babcock (English). Son of Babb (an old personal name); proud young Babb; Babb the cook.

Bachrach, Bacharach (German, Austrian). A person from Bacharach, meaning "a swampy place."

Backhaus (German, Austrian). A man who worked at the bakehouse, or who lived near a bakehouse.

Bacon (English). A man who raised pigs; a man who sold bacon and pork; a dweller at the signboard picturing the pig.

Baer, Bear (German, Austrian, English). A man who lived at the signboard of the bear; a man with bearlike strength.

Bailey (English, Scottish). An official of the lord of a manor.

Baird, Bard (Scottish, English). A bard or poet.

Baker (English). A person who made bread, usually the village baker.

Balaban (Ukrainian, Romanian, Jewish). A person who lived at the signboard of the falcon; a man who trained falcons.

Baldwin (English). Descendant of Baldwyn, a "steadfast friend."

Ballard (English). The bold strong man; the bald-headed man.

Balogh, Balog (Hungarian). A man who was left-handed; a man who shod horses.

Bancroft (English). *A person who lived near the bean croft or bean field.*

Baranowsky (Ukrainian). *A person who came from Baranow, "the place of rams."*

Barbarini (Italian). *Son of the young bearded man.*

Barclay, Barkeley, Berkeley, Berkley (English). *A person who lived near the "bercley" or "the birch-tree woods."*

Barker (English). *A leather worker who used tree bark for tanning.*

Barlow (English). *A person from Barlow, meaning "barley hill," "bare hill" or "boar hill."*

Barnhart, Barnhardt (German, Austrian, Swiss). *Son of Berin-hardt, meaning "powerful bear."*

Barr (Scottish). *A person whose homestead was at the top of the hill.*

Barrett, Barratt, Barat (English, French). *A person with bearlike strength.*

Barrios (Spanish). *A person who lived in the outskirts of a town.*

Barry (Irish). *A person from Barri in Normandy; a son of O'Beargha, meaning "the spearman."*

Bartkowski, Bartkowicz (Polish). *Son of Bartko, a pet form of Bartholomew, meaning "a turner of furrows" or "a farmer."*

Barton (English). *A person from Barton, meaning "barley farm."*

Baruch (Jewish). *Descendant of Baruch, meaning "blessed."*

Bates, Bateson (English). *Son of Bate, a pet form of Bartholomew, meaning "a turner of furrows" or "a farmer."*

Battaglia (Italian). *An aggressive warrior.*

Bauer (German, Austrian). *A tiller of the fields, a farmer.*

Baum (German, Austrian). *A person who lived near a prominent tree, probably a boundary marker.*

Baumgartner, Baumgart, Baumgarten (German, Austrian). *A man who owned an orchard.*

Bausch (German, Austrian). *A person who lived near a small hill or mound.*

Beaton, Beatty, Beattie (Scottish, English). *Descendant of young Bate, a pet form of Bartholomew. Bartholomew means a "tiller of furrows" or "a farmer".*

Beaupre (French). *A person from Beaupre, meaning "the beautiful meadow."*

Beauvais (French). *A person from Beauvais, meaning "the beautiful cleared lands."*

Beck (English, German, Norwegian). *A person who lived near a brook.*

Becker (German, Austrian). *A person who baked bread, usually the village baker.*

Bednarek, Bednarik (Polish, Czechoslovak). *A maker of barrels and casks.*

Bedrosian (Armenian). *Descendant of Bedros, a form of Peter, "the rock."*

Beethoven (German, Austrian). *A dweller on a farm where beets were grown.*

Belinsky (Russian). *Son of a fair-haired or light-complected man.*

Bell (English). *A person who lived at the signboard of the bell, usually a tavern; a handsome person; a descendant of Isabel, a form of Elizabeth.*

Bellini, Bellino (Italian). *Son of the handsome man.*

Benes (Czechoslovak). *The blessed one.*

Benjamin (Jewish). *The "Son of my right hand."*

Bennett (English). *A form of Benedict, meaning "the blessed one."*

Benoit (French, Belgian). *The young blessed one.*

Benson, Bensen (English). *Son of Benjamin, meaning "Son of my right hand;" son of Benno, meaning "the young bear."*

Bentley (English). *A person who lived near the bent-grass meadow.*

Berger, Bergeron (German, French). *The spearman; the mountaineer; the shepherd.*

Berglund (Swedish). *A mountain grove.*

Bergman, Bergmann (German, Austrian). A man who lived in the mountains, a mountaineer.

Bergstrom (Swedish). A mountain stream.

Berman (English, German, Austrian). Son of the bear hunter.

Bernard, Bernardi, Bernardino (English, French, Belgian, Italian). A man with bearlike strength; a name honoring St. Bernard.

Bernstein (German, Jewish). A person who dealt in amber; a person from the town of Bernstein.

Berry (English). A person who lived near a hill or a fortified place; a person from Berry in France.

Bevilacqua (Italian). A man who drank water, an abstainer from wine.

Beyer (German, Austrian). A person from Bavaria; a man as brave as a wild boar; a person who lived near the cattle shelter.

Bianco, Bianchi (Italian). A light-complected or white-haired man.

Bishop (English). A member of the bishop's retinue; a man who played the part of a bishop in church pageants.

Black (English). A person with a dark or swarthy complexion.

Blair (Scottish). A person whose house was in a plain or open field.

Blake (English, Irish). An ambiguous name, derived from Blaec, meaning "black" (dark-complected), or from Blac, meaning "white" (pale-complected).

Blanc, Blanchet (French). A man with blond or white hair.

Blanchard (French). A strong, blond-haired man, from Blanc-hard.

Blum, Blumm, Bloom (German, Dutch, Jewish). A person who raised flowers; a person who lived at the signboard picturing a flower.

Blumberg (German, Austrian, Jewish). A person who came from Blumberg, meaning "flower valley."

Blumenthal (German, Austrian, Jewish). A person who lived near "flower valley." Among Jewish families, "Blum-" usually honored a respected ancestress named Bluma, a popular given name.

Boch, Bochman, Bock, Bockman (German, Austrian, Swiss). A person whose shop sign pictured a buck deer or buck goat.

Boer (Dutch). A farmer who rented his land.

Boone (English). An honest, good man.

Booth (English). The herald; the person who owned or lived near the cattle shelter.

Borden (English). A person who lived near the valley of the wild boars.

Borg (Swedish, Norwegian). A person who lived near or in the castle or fort.

Borodin (Ukrainian). A son of the bearded man.

Boswell (English). A person from Bosville (forest village) in Normandy.

Boucher (French, Belgian). A butcher who cut and sold meat.

Boudreau (French, Belgian). Son of Batthar, "the army messenger."

Boulanger (French, Belgian). A person who baked and sold bread.

Bourgeois (French, Belgian). A town dweller.

Bouvier (French, Belgian). A man who tended cattle.

Bowers, Bower (English). A cottage owner and dweller.

Boyd (Irish, English). A yellow-haired person.

Boyer (French, Belgian). A bowman; a maker of bows; a cattle drover.

Boykin (Dutch, Jewish). A little boy or a small, mild-mannered man.

Boyle, O'Boyle (Irish). Descendant of Baorghill, meaning the "vain pledge."

Brady (Irish). Son of Bradaigh, "the high-spirited man."

Bradley (English). A person who came from Bradley, meaning "broad meadow."

Branca (Italian). A person whose shop had

a signboard picturing the claw of a bird or animal.

Brandeis, Brandes (German, Czechoslovak, Jewish). *A person who lived in a burnt clearing; a person who came from Brandeis in Bohemia.*

Brandon (English). *A person who lived near the beacon-fire or signal hill.*

Brennan, Brannon (Irish). *Descendant of Braon, "the sorrowful man," or of Branian, "the young raven." The raven was a symbol for a soldier.*

Brent (English). *A person who lived near or on the high hill.*

Bridges, Bridger, Briggs (Scottish, English). *A person who lived near the bridge.*

Brooks, Brooke (English). *A person who lived near a brook or spring.*

Brown, Browne (English, Scottish, Irish). *A person with a dark complexion; a descendant of Brun, meaning "brown."*

Broussard, Brousseau (French, Belgian). *A person who lived near the brushwood thicket.*

Bryant, Bryan (Irish). *Son of Bryan, "the strong one."*

Buchanan (Scottish). *A person from Buthchanain, "the home of the Canon." A canon was a churchman.*

Bukovich, Bukovic (Czechoslovak). *A person from Bukova, "the place of the beech trees."*

Burdick (English). *Son of Bourdit, the "young shield-bearer."*

Burgess (English). *A free citizen of a borough.*

Burke, Burk, Berke (Irish). *A person living in a stronghold or "burgh."*

Burnett (English). *A young brown-complected man.*

Burns, Burnes (Scottish, English, Irish). *A person who lived near a brook or burn.*

Burroughs, Burrows (English). *Son of the man who lived near the fort.*

Burton (English). *A person who came from Burton, a fortified village or farmstead.*

Butler (English, Irish). *The man in charge of the wine cellar, a butler.*

Byrd (English). *A person with birdlike characteristics; a person who lived at the signboard of the bird.*

Byrnes, Byrne (Irish). *Descendant of Bran, "the young raven." The raven was a symbol for a soldier.*

agney (Irish). *Descendant of Caigne, "the exactor of tribute."*

Caldwell, Caudill, Calwell (English). *A person who lived near the cool spring, from "Ceald-welle."*

Callaghan, Callahan (Irish). *Descendant of young Ceallach, meaning "strife or war."*

Cameron (Scottish). *A man with a crooked or hooked nose.*

Campbell (Scottish). *A man with a twisted mouth or arched lips.*

Cannon (Irish). *Descendant of Canain, meaning "the wolf cub."*

Cantore, Cantor (Italian, Jewish). *The soloist singer in a cathedral or synagogue.*

Capra, Capri, Caprio (Italian). *A man who lived at the signboard of the goat; a man with goat-like characteristics.*

Cardozo (Spanish, Portuguese). *A person who came from Cardoso, meaning "a place where thistles grew."*

Carlson, Carlsen (Swedish, Danish, Norwegian). *Son of Karl, meaning "the farmer," or son of Charles, "the manly one."*

Carleton (English). *A person from the farmer's homestead.*

Carlyle (English). *A person from Carlisle or Caer-luel, "the fortress tower."*

Carmichael (Irish). *Son of a follower of St. Michael.*

Carney (Irish). Descendant of Cearnaigh, "the victorious one."

Carpenter, Carpentier (English, French, Belgian). A man who worked with wood.

Carr (English, Irish, Scottish). A dweller near a rock, near a fort, or near a marsh.

Carroll (Irish). Descendant of Cearbhaill, meaning "the stag."

Carson (English, Scottish). Son of a servant; son of a person who lived near a rock, near a fort, or near a marsh.

Carver (English). A wood carver or sculptor, usually of religious objects.

Carter (English). A man who drove a cart.

Caruso (Italian). A man with close-cut hair.

Cary (Irish). The dark-complected man; the owner of fortresses.

Casey (Irish). Descendant of Cathasaigh, "the vigilant man."

Cassidy (Irish). Descendant of Caisidaigh, "the curly-haired man."

Castro (Spanish). A person who lived in or near the army camp.

Cavallo, Cavallaro (Italian). The man who had charge of horses; a man who lived at the signboard of the horse.

Cavanaugh, Kavanaugh (Irish). Descendant of Caomhanach, meaning "the handsome man."

Cermak (Czechoslovak). The person who lived at the signboard of the robin.

Cerny, Cherney, Czerny (Czechoslovak). A person with a swarthy complexion.

Cervantes (Spanish). A person from Cervantes, "the place of the stags."

Chandler (English). A candle-maker, later a ship's supplier.

Chapman (English). The travelling merchant.

Chase (English). The gamekeeper in a hunting park.

Chavez (Spanish). Son of a keymaker. Possibly son of Jaime, a form of James, meaning "the supplanter."

Christensen, Christenson, Christian (Danish, Norwegian, Swedish, English). Son of a Christian.

Churchill (English). A person who lived near the church on the hill.

Clancy (Irish). Son of Flannchadh, "the red-haired warrior."

Clark, Clarke (English, Irish). The scholar or scribe.

Clayton (English). A person whose homestead was built on clay soil.

Cleary, Clery (Irish). A scholar or historian from Clairaigh.

Cochran, Cochrane (Irish, Scottish). Descendant of the young counselor.

Cody (Irish). Descendant of Mac Oda, "son of the rich man."

Cohen, Cohn, Coen (Jewish). A priest descending from Aaron, the high priest. Aaron means "lofty mountain" or "exalted one."

Cole, Coles, Coleman, Collins (English). A descendant of Cole, a pet form of Nicholas, meaning "people's victory."

Coleman, Colman (Irish). Descendant of Colmain, meaning "little dove."

Collins (Irish, English). Son of Coilean, meaning "the hound's whelp;" son of Cole, a pet form of Nicholas, meaning "people's victory."

Columbo, Colombani, Colombini (Italian). Descendant of Colomb, meaning "the dove;" a person who raised doves; one who lived at the signboard of the dove.

Connelly, Connally, Connolly, Conley (Irish). Son of Congalaigh, "the valorous one."

Connors, Connor, Conner, Conners (Irish). Son of Conchobhair, meaning "the high-willed one;" or the son of Conchobar, meaning "the contentious one."

Conrad, Konrad (German, Austrian). The "bold counselor," from Kuon-rad.

Constantinescu (Romanian). Son of Constantine, meaning "the constant, steadfast one."

Conway (Irish, Scottish, Welsh). Descendant of Connmhaigh, "the young intelligent one."

Cook, Cooke (English). A person who prepared food.

Coolidge (English). A person who dwelled near the pool of cool water.

Cooper, Couper, Cowper (English). A person who made and sold casks, buckets and tubs.

Coppola (Italian). A descendant of Coppola, a form of Jacob, meaning "the supplanter."

Corbett (Irish, English). Descendant of Corbet, "the young raven." The raven was a symbol for a soldier.

Cornell (English). A person who lived near the cornel or dogwood tree. Probably a boundary marker.

Corregio, Correggio (Italian). A leather worker.

Cortez, Cortes (Spanish). A person who worked at the cattle corral; a courteous person; a person from Cortes.

Costello (Irish). Son of Mac Oisdealbh. Meaning is obscure. Possibly a battle cry calling on Os, an ancient pagan war god.

Coulter, Colter (English). The man responsible for raising and training a lord's young horses.

Cox, Coxe (English). A person who lived at the signboard of the cock; a cook.

Craig (Scottish, Irish). A person who lived near a prominent rock, probably a boundary marker.

Crane (English). A dweller at the signboard of the crane.

Crawford (Scottish, Irish). A person who dwelled at a river crossing where crows gathered.

Croix (French, Belgian). A person who lived near a wayside cross.

Cromwell (English). A person living near the crooked or winding stream.

Cronin (Irish). Son of Croinin, "the dark-complected man."

Cross (English). A person who lived near a wayside cross or shrine.

Crowley (Irish, English). Son of Cruadhlaigh, "the resolute hero;" a person living near the Craw-lea or "crow-meadow."

Cruz (Spanish, Portuguese). A person who lived near a wayside cross.

Cummings, Cummins (Irish, Scottish). Grandson of Cuimin. Meaning is obscure. Possibly the "small bent man."

Cuneo, Cunha (Spanish, Portuguese). Owner of a wedge-shaped or triangular piece of land.

Cunningham (Scottish). A person from Cunningham, meaning "the rabbit farm."

Currier (English). A person who dressed in fine leather.

Curtis, Curtiss (English). A courteous man.

Cushing (English). Son of Custance, the "constant, steady man."

ahlberg (Swedish). A mountain valley.

Dailey, Daley, Daly (Irish). Grandson of Dalaigh, "the frequenter of assemblies."

Dalton (English, Irish). A valley homestead.

D'Ambrosio (Italian). A form of Ambrose, meaning "immortal."

D'Angelo, De Angelo (Italian). A descendant of an angelic person.

Daniel, Daniels, Danielson (French, Belgian, English, Welsh). Of Daniel, meaning "God is my judge."

D'Arcy, Darcy, Darcey, Dorsey (French, Belgian, English, Irish). A person from Arcy in Normandy.

Davis, Davies, Davidson (English, Welsh). Son of Davis, a form of David, meaning "the commander" or "the beloved friend."

Dawson (English). Son of Daw, a form of David, meaning "commander" or "beloved friend."

Day, Daye (English, Welsh). A dairy owner; a shortened form of David, meaning "commander" or "beloved friend."

Dean, Deane (English). A cathedral official; a person who lived near the woodland pasture.

Debeer (Dutch). A person who dwelled at the signboard of the bear.

Decatur (Belgian). A person dwelling at the signboard of the cat.

Degas (French, Belgian). A person who lived in or near a forest.

De Gaulle (French, Belgian). A person who lived at the outer rampart of the fort.

De Gregorio (Italian). Son of Gregorio, "the watchful one."

De Jean (French, Belgian). Son of Jean, a form of John, meaning "Gracious gift of God."

De Jong, De Jonge, De Jonghe (Dutch). The young man or the younger son.

Delaney (Irish). Descendant of Dubhshlaine, "the dark-haired strong man."

Delehanty (Irish). Son of Dulchaointaigh, "the sad satirist."

De Luca (Italian). Son of Luca. A form of Luke, meaning "light."

De Marco (Italian). Son of Marco, a form of Mark. Mark is derived from Mars, the god of war.

Dembowski, Dembski (Polish). A person who lived near an oak tree, probably a boundary marker.

Demos (Greek). A pet form of Demosthenes, meaning "strong with people."

Dempsey (Irish). Son of O'Diomasaigh, "the proud man."

Derby (English). The caretaker of the deer enclosure or preserve.

Descartes (French). A family who lived in a suburban area.

Desjardines (French). A gardener, or a person living in a garden.

De Smet, De Smedt (Belgian, Dutch). The blacksmith.

Devereau, Devereaux (French, Belgian, Irish). A person from Evreux in Normandy.

De Vries (Dutch). A person from Friesland or "free land."

Dewey (Welsh). Son of Dewi, a form of David, meaning "commander" or "beloved friend."

Diaz, Dias (Spanish, Portuguese). Son of Diego. Diego is a form of Jacob, meaning "the supplanter."

Dietrich, Diedrich, Dietrick (German, Austrian). Forms of Theodoric, meaning "ruler of the people."

Dillon (Irish). A son of Young Dill, "the quiet one."

Dimitrov, Dimitroff (Bulgarian). Son of Dimitur, a form of Demeter, the goddess of fertility and harvests.

Dixon (English). Son of Dick, a form of Richard, meaning "strong ruler."

Dobrowski, Dobroski (Polish). Descendant of a good or virtuous man.

Dobry (Polish, Czechoslovak). A good and honest man.

Doherty, Dougherty, Daugherty (Irish). Son of Dochartaigh, the "unfortunate one."

Donahue, Donohue, Donaghue, Donoghue, Donohoe (Irish). Descendant of Donough or Donnchadha, meaning "dark warrior."

Donovan (Irish). Descendant of Donndamhan, "the brown-haired poet."

Dorsey (Irish, French). Descendant of Dorchaidne, "the dark one;" a person from Arcy in France.

Douglas (Scottish). A person who lived near the dark stream.

Doyle (Irish). Descendant of Dubhghall,

"the black foreigner." Probably a Norseman.

Drake *(English). A person who lived at the signboard of the dragon or who played the part of a dragon in pageants; a person who lived at the signboard of a drake or male duck.*

Drexel *(German, Austrian). A latheworker.*

Driscoll *(Irish). Descendant of Eidirsceol, "the mediator" or "the interpreter."*

Drummond *(Scottish). A person whose home was located near the ridge of hills.*

Du Bois, Dubosc, Duboscq *(French, Belgian). A person who lived near a small wood.*

Duclos *(French, Belgian). A person who lived near the fenced-in vineyard.*

Dudley *(English). The meadow of the man of the people.*

Duffy, Duffey *(Irish). Descendant of Dubhtaigh, "the dark one." Possibly a Norseman.*

Dugan, Duggan, Duigan *(Irish). Descendant of Dubhagain, "the young, dark one." Possibly a Norseman.*

Dumas *(French, Belgian). A person who lived in an isolated homestead.*

Dumont *(French, Belgian). A person who lived near the hill.*

Duncan *(Irish, Scottish). Descendant of Donnchad, "a brown warrior."*

Dunn, Dunne *(Irish). A brown-complected person; a grandson of Donn, meaning "brown."*

Dupont *(French, Belgian). A person who lived near the bridge.*

Dupree, Du Pree, Dupre *(French, Belgian). An owner of a meadow.*

Duran, Durand *(French, Belgian). Descendant of Durand, "the enduring man."*

Dusek *(Polish). Descendant of Dusk, meaning "little ghost."*

Duval *(French, Belgian). A person who lived in the valley.*

Dvorak *(Czechoslovak). A gentleman at the court of a nobleman.*

Dykes, Dykstra *(English, Dutch). A person who lived near the dike.*

**aton** *(English). A man whose farm was near a river.*

Edelman, Edelmann *(German, Austrian, Dutch, Jewish). The nobleman; the noble man; the husband of Edel or Adele, meaning "noble."*

Edison, Edson *(English). Son of Edie, a pet form of Edmund (protector of property), Edward (guardian of property) or Edwin (friend of property).*

Edmonds, Edmondson, Edmunds, Edmundson *(English). Son of Edmund, meaning "rich; protection." A dithematic usually interpreted as "protector of property."*

Edwards, Edward *(English). Son of Edward, meaning "rich; guard." A dithematic usually interpreted as "guardian of property."*

Ehrlich *(German, Austrian). An honest, honorable man.*

Einstein *(German, Austrian, Jewish). A builder with stone, a mason.*

Eisenberg, Isenberg *(German, Austrian, Jewish). A person from Eisenberg, meaning "iron mountain." Among Jews, Eise is a pet form of Isaac.*

Eisenhower, Eisenhauer *(German, Austrian). An iron cutter or iron miner.*

Elliott, Elliot, Ellis, Ellison *(English). Descendant of Elias, meaning "Jehovah is my god."*

Emerson *(English). Son of Emery, meaning "work ruler." Interpreted as meaning "foreman" or "overseer."*

Epstein, Eppstein *(German, Austrian, Jewish). A person who came from Eppstein, meaning "boar's stone."*

Erikson, Ericsson, Ericksen, Ericson *(Norwegian, Swedish). Son of Eric, "the ever-powerful one."*

Espinosa, Espinoza *(Spanish). A person*

who came from Espinosa, meaning "place of thorny thickets."

Esposito (Italian). A descendant of Esposito, meaning "an exposed foundling."

Evans, Evan (Welsh). Son of Evan, a form of John, meaning "Gracious gift of God."

Everett, Everhard (English). Literally boar; hard. A dithematic interpreted as "stalwart as a wild boar."

Ewing (English, Irish). The well-born man.

alconer, Falkner, Falknor, Faulkner (German, Austrian, English). A man who trained falcons or hawks.

Farley, Farleigh (Irish, English). A person whose homestead was located in a fern-covered clearing.

Farquhar, Farquharson (Scottish). Son of Farquhar, "the friendly man."

Farrell, O'Farrell, Ferrell (Irish). Descendant of Fearghail, "the fearless man."

Federenko, Federinko (Ukrainian). Descendant of Feodor, a form of Theodore, meaning "a gift of God."

Feinstein (German, Austrian, Jewish). Fine stone; a jeweler or dealer in precious gems.

Feldman, Feltman (German, Austrian, Jewish). A worker in the fields.

Ferenc (Hungarian). Ferenc is a form of Francis, meaning "free man."

Ferguson, Fergus (Scottish). Son of Fergus, "a man of great vigor."

Fernandez, Fernandes, Fernando (Spanish, Portuguese). Son of Fernando, meaning "adventurous journey" or "peaceful, brave man."

Ferrara, Ferrera (Italian). A person who came from Ferrara, meaning "the place of the foundry."

Ferraro, Ferrari, Ferrero (Italian). The blacksmith or horse-shoer.

Fields, Field, Fielding (English). An owner of open fields.

Finley, Finlay (Irish, Scottish). Son of Fionnlaigh, "the fair hero."

Finn (Irish). Son of Fionn, "the fair one."

Fischer, Fisher (German, Austrian, English). A person who caught or sold fish.

Fitzgerald (Irish). Son of Gerald, meaning "strong spear."

Fitzpatrick (Irish). Son of Patrick, meaning "noble" or "patrician."

Fitzsimmons, Fitzsimons (Irish). Son of Simon, meaning "one who hears."

Flaherty (Irish). Grandson of Flaithbheartaigh, meaning "the bright ruler."

Flanagan (Irish). Descendant of Flann, meaning "the red-haired man."

Fleming (English, Scottish, Irish). A man from Flanders, a Fleming.

Fletcher (English). An arrow-maker.

Flores, Florez (Spanish). A person who grew flowers.

Floyd (Welsh). Descendant of Lloyd, "the gray-haired one."

Flynn, Flinn (Irish). Descendant of Flionn, meaning "the red-haired or ruddy-complected man."

Foley (Irish). Descendant of Foghladha, meaning "the plunderer."

Fonseca (Spanish). A person who lived near a dry spring.

Fontaine (French, Belgian). A person who lived by the spring.

Forbes (Scottish). Son of Forba, an "owner of fields."

Ford, Forde (English). A person who lived at the stream crossing.

Foreman, Forman (English). A bailiff or overseer of an estate.

Foster, Forrest, Forrester (English). A forest warden; a gamekeeper.

Fournier (French, Belgian). A person who baked bread; a baker.

Fowler (English). A bird-catcher or a gamekeeper.

Fox, Foxe, Foxx (English). A person who

lived at the signboard of the fox; a person with foxlike qualities.

Francis, Francois, Franco, Francisco, Francheschi (English, French, Belgian, Spanish, Italian). Son of Francis. Francis means "the free man."

Franck, Frank, Franke (German, Austrian). A person from Franconia in Germany; a free man.

Franklin, Franklyn (English). A well-to-do freeholder.

Franz, Frantz, Frankovich, Franczak (Austrian, German, Polish). Son of Francis, meaning "the free man."

Fraser, Frasier, Frazer, Frazier (Scottish). A person from Frisia; a person from the place where strawberries grew.

Frederick, Frederik, Fredericks (German, Austrian). Son of Frederick, meaning "the peaceful ruler."

Frederickson, Frederikson, Fredericksen, Frederiksen (Swedish, Danish, Norwegian). Son of Frederick, meaning "the peaceful ruler."

Freeman (English). A free man or yeoman who owned land.

Frey (Norwegian, German, Austrian). A worshipper of Frey, the Norse god of fruitfulness; a freeman.

Friedman, Friedmann (German, Austrian, Jewish). Forms of Friduman, meaning "a peaceful man." Adopted by Jews to represent Solomon, meaning "man of peace."

Frisch, Fritsch (German, Austrian). A young freeman.

Fuchs (German, Austrian). A hunter of foxes; a person who lived at the signboard of the fox; a person with foxlike qualities.

Fullerton, Fulton (English). The homestead of a raiser of fowl or poultry.

**abor** (Hungarian). A form of Gabriel, meaning "man of God."

Gagnon, Gagnier, Gagne (French, Belgian). A farmer who owns his land.

Gaines, Gaynes (English). A straightforward person.

Gallagher, Gallegher, Gallaher (Irish). Son of Gallchobhair, meaning "foreign helper." Probably a Norseman.

Gallo, Galli (Italian). Nickname given to a man who strutted like a rooster; a person who lived at the signboard of the rooster.

Galvez (Spanish). Son of the chanter; a person from Galvez, meaning "the white falcon."

Gamble (English). A wise old man.

Garcia (Spanish, Portuguese). Descendant of Garcia, "a spearman."

Gardner, Gardiner (English, French, Belgian). A person who tended a garden.

Garfield (English). A person who lived near the grassy land or pasture.

Garnier, Garner (French, English). An army scout or sentinel.

Garrett (English). The brave spearman.

Garrison (English). Son of the spearman.

Gatto, Gattone, Gatti (Italian). A person living at the signboard of the cat; a person possessing the qualities of a cat.

Gautier, Gauthier (French, Belgian). Descendant of Gautier, an "army ruler."

Gavilan (Spanish). A person living at the signboard of the sparrow hawk.

Gentile (Italian). A well-bred, gentle person; a person of noble birth.

Georges, George (French, Belgian, Welsh). Son of George, meaning "the farmer."

Georgi, Georgieff, Georgiev, Georgopoulos, Georgovich (Bulgarian, Greek, Russian). See **Georges**.

Georgescu (Romanian). See **Georges**.

Gerard, Girard, Giraud, Gerardi, Girardi (French, Belgian, English, Italian). Son of Gerard, meaning "strong spear."

Gilbert, Gilbertson, Gibson (English). Descendant of Gilbert, meaning "bright pledge."

Gilmore, Gilmer, Gilmour (Irish, Scot-

tish). A person devoted to Mary, the Blessed Mother.

Ginsberg, Ginsburg (German, Austrian, Jewish). A person who came from Gunzburg or "Gunz's stronghold."

Giroux (French, Belgian). Descendant of Giroux, meaning "spear; wolf."

Glenn, Glen (English, Scottish). A person who lived in the small valley.

Goldberg, Goldberger (German, Austrian, Jewish). A person from Goldberg or "gold mountain."

Goldman (English, German, Austrian, Jewish). An artisan who worked in gold; a descendant of Golda, an ancestress.

Goldsmith (English). A jeweler who made and sold articles of gold.

Goldstein (German, Austrian, Jewish). A jeweler who used a goldstone, a touchstone to test gold.

Gomez, Gomes (Spanish, Portuguese). The path of man; the young warrior.

Gonzalez, Gonzales (Spanish, Portuguese). The young warrior, from the Gothic word Gunzo.

Goodman (English). An upright, good man; the head of a household; an army guard.

Goodwin (English). A descendant of Godwin, meaning "God's friend" or "God's protection."

Gordon, Gorden, Gordan (Scottish, English, Russian, Jewish). A person who lived on a wedge-shaped piece of land; a person who came from Grodno (the fortified place) in Russia.

Gorman (Irish). Descendant of Gormain, meaning "the blue-eyed one" or "the one dressed in blue."

Grabowski, Grabowsky (Polish). A person who came from Grabow, "the place of elms."

Graham, Grahame (Scottish). A person who lived in the gray homestead.

Grant (English, Scottish). A heavy man or great man.

Grassi, Grasso (Italian). A large, fleshy man.

Graves (English). A person whose homestead was in a grove of trees.

Gray, Graye (English, French, Belgian). A gray-haired man.

Grecco, Greco (Italian, Spanish). A man from Greece.

Green, Greene (English). A person living near the village green.

Greenberg, Greenburg (German, Austrian, Jewish). A person who came from Greenberg, meaning "green mountain."

Gregorich, Gregorovitch (Yugoslav, Russian). Son of Gregory, meaning "the vigilant one."

Gregory, Gregg, Gregoire, Gregorio (English, Scottish, French, Italian). Son of Gregory, "the vigilant one."

Griffin, Griffen (Welsh, Irish). A person who lived at the signboard of the griffin (an heraldic half-lion, half-eagle creature); a person with a ruddy face or red hair.

Grodsky, Grodecki, Grodinsky, Grodzicki, Grodnitzky (Polish, Russian). A person who lived or worked in a castle.

Gronski, Gronsky (Polish). A member of a group, guild or assembly.

Gross, Grossman (German, Austrian, Jewish). A large and heavy man.

Grosvenor (English). The great hunter. From the French Gros-veneur.

Grunwald, Grunewald (German, Austrian). A person who lived in the green forest.

Guerrero (Spanish). A foot soldier, from the Teutonic Werra.

Guillaume (French, Belgian). A French form of William, meaning "resolution; helmet." Usually interpreted as "resolute protector."

Gulbrandsen, Gulbransen (Danish). Son of Gull-brand, meaning "the golden fire-brand."

Gunther (German, Austrian). Battle warrior, from Gunt-hari.

Guttenberg, Guttenberger (German, Austrian). *A person from Guttenberg, meaning "pleasant mountain."*

Guzman, Gusman *(Spanish, Portuguese). A good or godly man, from the Gothic words "Gods-man." Later Guzman came to mean "nobleman."*

aas, Haase *(German, Austrian). A person who lived at the signboard of the hare; a person with the mannerisms of a hare.*

Hahn *(German, Austrian). A person who lived at the signboard of the cock; a person with the strutting characteristics of a cock.*

Haines, Haynes *(English). A man who owned or lived near hedged fields.*

Haldemann, Haldeman *(Swiss, German, Austrian). A person living on the mountainside; a person who came from Halden in Switzerland.*

Halevy, Halevi *(Jewish). A man from the tribe of Levy; a priest's assistant.*

Hall, Halle *(English, German, Austrian). A servant in the manor house; a person who came from Halle (salt-works) in Germany.*

Hallahan *(Irish). Descendant of young Aille, "the handsome man."*

Hamilton *(English, Scottish). A person from Hambleton, meaning a "farmstead on a treeless hill."*

Hammerstein *(German, Austrian, Jewish). A person from Hammerstein, meaning "a large stone homestead."*

Hammond, Hammon, Hammonds *(English). Descendant of Heah-mund, meaning "the home protector."*

Hancock *(English). Descendant of little Han, a pet form of John, meaning "Gracious gift of God."*

Hanley, Handley *(Irish). Descendant of Hainle, "the handsome one."*

Hansen, Hanson, Hanssen *(Danish, Swedish, Norwegian). Son of Hans, a pet form of John, "Gracious gift of God."*

Harding, Harden *(English). Descendant of Hardwin, meaning "firm friend."*

Hardy, Hardie *(English). The daring, strong one, from Hardi.*

Harmon, Harman *(English). Descendant of Herman, "the army warrior."*

Harris, Harrison *(Scottish, Welsh, English). Son of Harry, a form of Henry, meaning "home ruler" or "estate ruler."*

Hart, Harte *(English). A person living at the sign of the hart or stag.*

Hartley *(English). A person who lived near the meadow of the red hart.*

Hartman, Hartmann *(English, Dutch). A strong, hearty man.*

Harvey *(Irish, English, Scottish). The cattle owner; the army fighter.*

Hauptmann, Hauptman *(German, Austrian). A village leader, later an army captain.*

Hauser *(German, Austrian). A tenant in a house.*

Hausmann, Hausman *(German, Austrian). A house servant, usually in a nobleman's household.*

Havenmeyer *(German, Austrian). A magistrate or judge.*

Havlik, Havlick, Havlicek *(Czechoslovak, Ukrainian). Son of Havlik, a form of Gabriel, meaning "the strong man of God."*

Havranek *(Czechoslovak). A farm worker; the owner or manager of a farm.*

Hawkins, Hawkinson *(English). Son of young Haw, a pet form of Harry or Henry, meaning "home ruler" or "estate ruler."*

Hayden, Haydon, Heyden *(English). A person from a hay valley.*

Hayes, Hayward *(English). The hay warden who was responsible for repairing a village's hedges and fences.*

Healy, Healey *(Irish, English). A clever, skillful man, from Heilidhi; a homestead on a high meadow, from Heah-leah.*

Heath *(English). An owner of uncultivated heath land.*

Hegy, Hegyi *(Hungarian). A person who lived near or on a mountain.*

Heiden, Heiser (German, Austrian). A person living near or on uncultivated heath land or heather land.

Heifetz (Jewish). Descendant of Chaifetz, meaning "desire" or "gift;" a person who came from Haifa in Israel.

Heilman, Heilmann, Heileman (German, Austrian). A healthy, hearty man.

Hein, Heine, Heineman, Heinsohn, Heinzelman (German, Austrian). An owner of protected or fenced property.

Heinrich, Heinrichs, Heinz, Heintz (German, Austrian). See **Henry.**

Heller, Hellerman (German, Austrian). A person whose home was on a hill; a hardy-fighting warrior.

Hendricks, Hendrick, Hendrich, Henrick, Hendrix (German, Austrian). See **Henry.**

Henley (English). A person who lived in the clearing in the high wood.

Hennessey, Hennessy (Irish). A descendant of Aonghus, meaning "the only choice" or "the one choice."

Henrici (Italian, German, Austrian). See **Henry.**

Henry, Henderson, Henri (English, Scottish, French, Belgian). Son of Henry, meaning "home ruler" or "estate ruler."

Herman, Herrmann (German, Austrian). Descendant of the army warrior.

Hernandez (Spanish). Son of Hernando, meaning "adventurous journey," or "a peaceful, brave man."

Herrara, Herrero (Spanish). A worker in iron, a smith.

Hertz (German, Austrian, Jewish). Hertz means heart or hart in German. As a name, it means a brave person, a beloved person or a person living at the signboard of the hart.

Herzog (German, Austrian). An army leader from Hari-zogon.

Hewitt, Hewett, Hewlett (English). A descendant of Hew or Hugh, meaning "the intelligent one."

Heydendael, Heydendall, Heidendael,

Heidendall (Dutch). A person who lived in a heather-covered valley.

Hickey (Irish). Son of Hicidhe, meaning "the healer or doctor."

Higgins (English, Irish). Son of young Higg or Hick, pet forms of Richard, "the powerful ruler."

Hill, Hills (English). A dweller near or on a hill.

Hirsch, Hirsh (German, Austrian, Jewish). A person who lived at the signboard of the hart; a name adopted by Jews as a symbol of the Israelite tribe of Naphtali.

Hodges, Hodge (English). Son of Hodge, a pet form of Roger, the "famous spearman."

Hoffman, Hoffmann (German, Austrian). A manager or owner of a large farm.

Hogan (Irish). Son of Og, meaning "the young one" or "the youth."

Holloway (English). A person whose home was near a sunken road or ditch, probably a boundary line.

Holmes (English). A person who lived on a river island.

Hoover (German, Austrian, Swiss). A farmer who owned his own land.

Hopkins, Hopkinson (English). Son of young Hob, a pet form of Robert, meaning "bright fame."

Horowitz, Horwitz, Horvitz (Czechoslovak, Russian, Jewish). A man from Horice or Horitz (mountainous place) in Bohemia; the son of the mountaineer.

Horvath, Horvat, Horwath (Hungarian). A man from Croatia.

Houston, Huston (English, Scottish). A person from Hugh's-ton, "the homestead of the intelligent one."

Howard (English). The chief warden; the high guardian.

Howell, Howells (English, Welsh). Son of the prominent man; son of the young man.

Hruska (Czechoslovak). A person who lived near the pear tree.

Hubbard (English). Descendant of Hubert, meaning "brilliant intellect."

Hudson (English). Son of Hudde, a pet form of Richard, meaning "strong ruler;" a son of Hod, meaning "the hooded one."

Huffman (German, Austrian). A farm worker; servant of the intelligent, free man.

Hughes, Hugo, Huguelet (Welsh, Irish, English, German, Austrian, French, Belgian). Son of Hu or Hugh, meaning "the highly intelligent one."

Humphrey, Humphries, Humphreys (Welsh, English). A descendant of "the peaceful giant," from hun-frid.

Hunt, Hunter, Hunte (English). A hunts-man.

Hyde (English). Owner of a hide of land, enough to support one family.

**banez** (Spanish). Son of Iban, a form of John, meaning "Gracious gift of God."

Ingram (English). Son of Ing's raven. Ing was a mythological pagan hero, and the raven was a symbol for a soldier.

Innes, Inness (Scottish). The son of Aonghus, meaning "one choice" or "the only choice."

Ionescu (Romanian). Son of John, meaning "Gracious gift of God."

Irvin, Irving, Irvine (Scottish, English). Meaning is obscure. Possible meanings: "white river;" "green river."

Isaacson, Isaac, Isaacs (Jewish, German, Austrian, English). Son of Isaac, meaning "the one who laughs."

Ivan, Ivanoff, Ivanov, Ivanow (Russian, Bulgarian, Czechoslovak, Ukrainian, Yugoslav). A descendant of Ivan, a Slavic form of John, meaning "Gracious gift of God."

Iverson, Iversen (Swedish, Danish, Norwegian). A son of Iver, meaning "the archer."

**ablonski, Jablonsky** (Polish). A person who lived near the apple tree, probably a boundary marker.

Jackson (English). Son of Jack, a pet form of John, meaning "Gracious gift of God."

Jacobi, Jacoby (French, Belgian, German, Austrian, Jewish). See **Jacobs.**

Jacobs, Jacobson, Jacobsen (English, Danish, Norwegian, Swedish). Descendant of Jacob, meaning "the supplanter."

James, Jamieson (English, Scottish). A descendant of James, a form of Jacob, meaning "the supplanter."

Janecek, Janczak, Janiak, Jankowski, Janowicz (Polish). Son of Jan or John, meaning "Gracious gift of God."

Janos, Janisch, Jankovic (Hungarian, German, Czechoslovak, Yugoslav). See **Janecek.**

Jantzen, Jansen, Janson (Dutch, Danish, Norwegian, Swedish). See **Janecek.**

Jarecki (Polish). The lord of the village of Jarek, or a person who came from Jarek.

Jarvis (English). The eager spearman.

Jaworski, Jaworowski (Polish). One who came from the village of Jaworow, meaning "maple tree."

Jefferson, Jeffries, Jefferies (English). Descendant of Geoffrey or Jeffrey, meaning "God's peace."

Jenkins, Jenkinson, Jennings (Welsh, Scottish, English). Son of little Jen, a pet form of John, meaning "Gracious gift of God."

Jensen, Jenssen (Danish, Norwegian). Son of Jens, a pet form of John, meaning "Gracious gift of God."

Jimenez, Jiminez (Spanish). Son of Simon, meaning "one who hears or hearkens."

Johanson, Johansen, Johannsen, Johansson (Swedish, Norwegian, Danish). See **Johnson.**

Johnson, Johnsen, Johnsson (English, Danish, Norwegian, Swedish). Son of John, meaning "Gracious gift of God."

Johnston, Johnstone (English, Welsh). A person from John's town or manor.

Joliet (French, Belgian). Son of young Joli, "the good-looking one."

Jolson (Jewish). Son of Joel, meaning "Jehovah is God."

Jones (Welsh, English). Son of Jone, a Welsh form of John, meaning "Gracious gift of God."

Jordan, Jorden, Jourdain, Jordon (English, French, Belgian). Descendant of Jordan or Jourdain, meaning "a river flowing downward;" a name given to a pilgrim to the Jordan River in Palestine or to a person baptized with its waters.

Jorgenson, Jorgensen, Jergenson, Jurgensen (Danish, Norwegian). Son of George, meaning "the farmer."

Jovanovic, Jovanovich (Yugoslav). Son of Jovan or John, meaning "Gracious gift of God;" a dweller near an alder tree, probably a boundary marker.

Joyce (English, Irish). A joyous, agreeable person.

Judson (English). Son of Jude, meaning "the praised one."

 **afka** (Czechoslovak). A person who lived at the signboard of the jackdaw.

Kagan, Kaganovich, Kaganoff (Jewish). Descendant of a priest.

Kahn, Kahan (German, Austrian, Jewish). A young opponent; a boatman; descendant of a priest.

Kaiser, Kayser, Keyser, Kiser (German, Austrian). Kaiser means Ceasar or emperor. The name was given to men who played the emperor in church pageants or who acted in a haughty manner.

Kalish, Kalisz (Polish). A person who came from the village of Kalisz.

Kallinen (Finnish). Son of Charles, meaning "the manly one."

Kaminski, Kaminsky (Polish, Russian). A dweller near a stone castle or a stone boundary marker.

Kane, Keane (Irish). Descendant of Cathan, meaning "the warrior."

Kaplan (Jewish). Descendant of a priest.

Karlson, Karlsen (Swedish). Son of Karl, meaning "the farmer," or son of Charles, meaning "the manly one."

Karras, Karas (Greek, Estonian). A person with a swarthy complexion.

Kasper (German, Austrian). The horseman; the master of the treasure.

Katz (Jewish). An abbreviation of Kohen Tzedek, meaning "priest of righteousness."

Kaufman, Kaufmann, Kauffman, Kauffmann (German, Austrian). A merchant or tradesman.

Kearney, Carney (Irish). Descendant of Cearnaigh, "the victorious one."

Kearns (Irish). Descendant of Ciarain, "the black-haired one."

Kelleher (Irish). Descendant of Cailachair, meaning "the loving companion."

Keller, Kellerman (German, Austrian). The owner of a tavern or the keeper of a wine cellar.

Kelly, Kelley, O'Kelly, O'Kelley (Irish). Descendant of Ceallaigh, meaning "strife."

Kemeny (Hungarian). The austere and hard man.

Kennedy (Irish, Scottish). Descendant of Cinneide, meaning "ugly head." Probably describes a helmeted warrior.

Kerouac, Kirouac (French). A person who lived near the harbor surrounded by cliffs. From the Breton, Ker-houart.

Kerr (English, Irish). A person who lived near low, marshy land or near a fort.

King (English). A man who played the part of the king in a play; a person in the king's household; a person with kingly manners or qualities.

Kirk (Scottish, Irish). A person who lived near a church.

Kirkegaard (Danish). A person whose house was near the churchyard.

Klaus (German, Austrian). Descendant of Klaus, a pet form of Nicholaus or Nicholas, meaning "victorious army man."

Klein, Kleine (German, Austrian). A small man or a neat man.

Knapp (English). *A person who lived on a hilltop.*

Knight (English, Welsh). *A well-born man who held land in exchange for military service; a young retainer.*

Knowles, Knollton (English). *A person whose home was on a hilltop or knoll.*

Knox (Scottish, English). *A person who lived on or near a hill, from the Gaelic word Cnoč.*

Knudsen, Knudson, Knutsen, Knutson (Danish, Norwegian, Swedish). *Son of Knut or Canute. A warrior's name. Possible meanings: knot; hill; white-haired.*

Koch (German, Austrian). *A person who prepared food, a cook.*

Kocsis (Hungarian). *A carter or coachman.*

Koehler, Koeller, Kohler (German, Austrian). *A person who burned charcoal; a coal worker.*

Konstantopoulos (Greek). *Son of Konstantinos, a form of Constantine, meaning "the steadfast man."*

Korshak, Korsak (Ukrainian). *A dweller at the signboard of the korshak, a bird of the eagle family.*

Kosciusko (Polish). *Descendant of Koseia or Konstanty, meaning "the steadfast man."*

Kovac, Kovacs, Kovatch, Kovach (Hungarian). *Son of the metal-worker or smith.*

Kovalenko (Ukrainian). *Son of the metal-worker or smith.*

Kowal, Kowalski, Kowalewski (Polish). *Son of the metal-worker or smith.*

Kraft (German, Austrian). *A strong and courageous man.*

Kramer, Cramer (German, Austrian). *A merchant or tradesman.*

Krause, Krauss, Kraus, Crouse (German, Austrian). *A curly-haired man.*

Kroeger, Kroger (Dutch). *An innkeeper or tavern owner.*

Krueger, Kruger, Krug, Krugman (German, Austrian). *An innkeeper or tavern owner.*

Kruschev (Russian). *A person with the characteristics of a beetle.*

Kuhn, Kuehn, Kuntz (German, Austrian). *A bold, keen-witted man; a descendant of Kunrat, meaning "the bold counselor."*

Kurowski (Polish). *A person who came from the town of Kurowo, meaning "rooster."*

Kuykendall, Kuykendoll (Dutch). *A dweller in the valley which abounded in chickens or wild fowl.*

 *a Croix* (French, Belgian). *A person who lived near a roadside cross; a crusader.*

La Fayette (French, Belgian). *A person living near the beech grove.*

Lambert (English, French). *From Landberaht, a dithematic name meaning "land; bright." Usually interpreted as "famous for his land."*

Lane (English). *A person who lived near a path or rural road.*

Lang, Lange (English, Dutch, German, Austrian, Swedish, Danish, Norwegian). *A very tall man.*

Larson, Larsen, Larsson (Swedish, Danish, Norwegian). *Son of Lars, a form of Lawrence. See Lawrence.*

Lawrence, Laurence, Laurent, Laurie (English, French, Belgian, Scottish). *Son of Lawrence, meaning "laurel-crowned." The laurel wreath was a symbol of victory.*

Lawson (English). *Son of Law, a pet form of Lawrence. See Lawrence.*

Leahy (Irish). *A son of O Laochdha, "the heroic man."*

Le Brun (French, Belgian). *A dark-complected or brown-haired person.*

Le Clair, Leclaire (French, Belgian). *A person who is quick to act; a person with a clear complexion.*

Leclerc, Le Clercq (French, Belgian). *A clergyman; a learned man or scholar.*

Le Corbusier (Swiss, French, Belgian). A person who made and sold baskets.

Le Doux, Ledoux (French, Belgian). A pleasant, gentle person.

Lee (English). A person who lived near the meadow or pastureland.

Le Febre, Le Febvre, Le Fevre (French, Belgian). A worker in metals, or a smith.

Lehmann, Lehman (German, Austrian). A free man who was the tenant of a nobleman.

Leonard (English, French, Belgian, Irish). From Leon-hard, meaning "powerful as a lion;" from Leannan, meaning "wearer of a cloak."

Levigne, Levine (French, Belgian, German, Austrian). A vineyard owner or worker.

Levy, Levi, Levine, Levin (Jewish). Son of Levi, meaning "united."

Lewandowski, Lewan (Polish). A person who came from Lewandow, meaning "Lewand's village."

Lewis (Welsh, English). A renowned warrior; a regal man.

Lieberman, Liebermann (German, Austrian, Jewish). The beloved servant; the beloved warrior. Also a synonym for Eliezer, meaning "God is our help."

Liebowitz, Leibowitz (German, Austrian, Jewish). Son of Lieb, "the loved one."

Lincoln (English). A person from Lincoln, which means "the lake colony."

Lippman, Lipman (German, Austrian). A servant of Lipp, a pet form of Philip. Philip means "the lover of horses."

Liska (Czechoslovak). A person who lived at the signboard of the fox; a person with the characteristics of a fox.

Liszt (Hungarian). A dealer in flour.

Little, Littell (English). A small or short man.

Llewellyn, Llewellin (Welsh). Descendant of Llewellyn, meaning "the lion-like man."

Lloyd (Welsh). The gray-haired man, from the root word Lloyd.

Lombardo, Lombardi (Italian). A person who came from Lombardia, the country of the Lombards.

Long (English). An exceptionally tall man.

Lopez, Lopaz (Spanish). Son of Lope or Lupe, meaning "the wolf."

Lorenzo, Lorenzi (Spanish, Italian). A descendant of Lorenzo, a form of Lawrence, meaning "laurel-crowned." The laurel wreath was a symbol of victory.

Lowe, Loew, Loewy (English, Austrian, German, Jewish). A person living at the signboard of the lion; a person with lion-like characteristics; a descendant from the tribe of Judah.

Lowery (Irish, Scottish). Son of Labhrada, meaning the spokesman.

Lowrie, Lowry, Lowrey (Scottish). Descendant of Lowrie, a form of Lawrence, meaning "laurel-crowned." The laurel wreath was a symbol of victory.

Lucas, Lucca, Luciano, Lukas (English, French, Italian, Polish). Son of Luke, meaning "light."

Lundquist (Swedish). Grove, twig.

Lupo, Lupa, Lupi, Luppo (Italian). A dweller at the signboard of the wolf; a greedy, voracious person.

Lustig (German, Austrian). A cheerful, merry man.

Luther (German, Austrian). Descendant of Lothaire, "the famous warrior;" "the lute player."

Lynch (Irish). From the Norman place name of de Lench, or from the Gaelic Loingseach, meaning "the mariner."

Lyons, Lyon (English, Scottish, French). Son of Leon, meaning "the lion;" a dweller at the signboard of the lion.

*acDougall, MacDowell* (Scottish). Son of Dubh-ghaill, meaning "the dark foreigner," probably a Norseman.

MacFadden, McFadden, McFayden (Scottish, Irish). Son of young

Pad, a pet form of Patrick, meaning "the patrician."

MacFarland, MacFarlane, MacFarlan, MacPartland (Scottish, Irish). Son of Pharlain, meaning "ocean waves."

MacGregor, McGregor (Scottish). Son of Greagair or Gregory, meaning "the watchful one."

MacKenzie, McKenzie (Scottish). Son of Coinneach, meaning "the fair one."

MacLean, MacLane, MacLain (Scottish). Son of a follower of St. John, from Mac-Giolla-Eain.

MacMillan (Scottish, Irish). Son of Mac-Maolain, "the bald or tonsured man."

MacPerson (Scottish). Son of the parson.

Madden (Irish). Son of Madain, meaning "the hound."

Madison (English). Son of Mad. Mad is a form of Matthew, which means "Gift of God."

Maguire (Irish). Son of the pale or light-complected man.

Mahoney, Mahony (Irish). Descendant of Mathghamhain, meaning "the bear."

Majewski (Polish). A person born in May.

Maki (Finnish). A person who lived on or near a hill.

Malenkov (Russian). Son of the little man.

Mallory, Malory (English). A sad or unfortunate man.

Malloy (Irish). Son of "the noble chief," from Maolmhuaidh.

Malone (Irish). Son of Maoil-Eoin, "a follower of St. John."

Mann, Manning (German, English, Irish). Descendant of "the man" or "the hero;" descendant of Mathghamhna, meaning "one with the strength of a bear."

Marcus, Marco, Marconi (English, Italian). Descendant of Marcus or Mark, meaning "the warlike one." Derived from Mars, the Roman god of war.

Marek (Polish). See **Mark.**

Margolis, Margolies, Margoles (Jewish, Ukrainian, Russian). Descendant of Margolis or Margaret, meaning "the pearl."

Marino, Marinaro (Italian). The sailor.

Mark, Marks, Marx (French, Belgian, English, German, Austrian). Son of Mark, meaning "the warlike one." Among Christians, the name honored St. Mark, the Evangelist.

Markopoulos, Markowitz, Markowski, Marko (Greek, Polish, Ukrainian). See **Mark.**

Marshall (English). The man in charge of the horses; a high ranking military official.

Martin, Marten, Martineau, Martini, Martinelli, Martinez (French, Belgian, Welsh, English, Italian, Spanish). Son of Martin, meaning "the warlike one." The name honored St. Martin, the soldier-saint.

Masaryk (Czechoslovak). The little butcher.

Mason (English). The builder with stone or brick.

Matthews, Matthias, Matuszak, Matyas (English, German, Polish, Hungarian). Son of Matthew. Matthew means "Gift of God."

Mattson, Matteson (Swedish). Son of Matt, a pet form of Matthew, meaning "Gift of God."

Mauriac (French, Belgian). A person from the estate of Maurius.

Maurois (French, Belgian). The dark-complected man.

Maxwell (Scottish). A person who lived near Maccus-welle, meaning "well of the good ruler."

Mayer (German, Austrian). The steward or head servant; later a free farmer.

McAuliffe (Irish). Son of Olaf, meaning "ancestral relics."

McCarthy, McCarty, MacCarthy (Irish). Son of Carthaigh, meaning "the loving man."

McConnell (Irish). Son of Domhnaill, meaning "mighty in the world."

McCormick, McCormack, McCormac, MacCormick (Irish). *Son of Cormac, meaning "the charicteer."*

McCoy, MacCoy (Irish). *Son of Aodh, meaning "fire" or "firebrand."*

McDaniel, McDaniels, MacDaniel, Mac-Daniels (Irish, Scottish). *Son of Domhnaill, meaning "mighty in the world."*

McDermott, MacDermott (Irish, Scottish). *Son of Diarmid or Dermot, "the free man."*

McDonald, Macdonald, McDonnell, Mc-Donell (Scottish, Irish). *Son of Donald, meaning "the dark-haired stranger;" son of Domhnaill, meaning "mighty in the world."*

McDonough, MacDonough (Irish, Scottish). *Son of Donnchadh, "the strong, brown warrior."*

McGee (Irish). *Son of Aodh, meaning "fire" or "firebrand."*

McGinnis, Macginnis, Maginnis (Irish). *Son of Aonghus, meaning "the single choice."*

McGovern, MacGovern (Irish). *Son of Eamhradh, meaning "born in summer."*

McGowan, MacGowan, McGowen (Irish, Scottish). *The son of Ghobhan, "the smith or metal-worker.*

McGrath, McGraw (Irish). *Son of Craith, "the prosperous one."*

McGuire, MacGuire, Maguire (Irish). *A son of the pale man.*

McIntyre, MacIntyre (Irish, Scottish). *From Mac-an-Tsaoir, meaning "son of the carpenter."*

McKay, MacKay (Irish, Scottish). *Son of Aodh, meaning "fire" or "firebrand."*

McKenna, MacKenny, McKinney, McKennay (Irish). *Son of Cionaodha, meaning "beloved of the fiery one."*

McKinley, MacKinley (Irish, Scottish). *Son of Fionnlaigh, "the fair-haired hero."*

McLoughlin, McLaughlin, MacLoughlin, MacLachlan (Irish, Scottish). *Son of Lachlainn, meaning "the man from the land of lakes."*

McMahon, McMahan (Irish). *Son of Mathghamhain, meaning "the bear."*

McNamara (Irish). *Son of Conmara, meaning "the hound of the sea."*

Meir (Jewish). *The enlightened, learned man.*

Melchior, Melchiore, Melchiorre (French, German, Italian). *A descendant of Melchior or the "king of light."*

Mendelsohn, Mendelson, Mendelssohn (German, Austrian, Jewish). *Son of Mendel, meaning "a man of intellect and wisdom."*

Mendoza (Portuguese, Spanish). *A person from Mendoza, meaning "high mountains."*

Meredith (Welsh). *Descendant of the sea lord.*

Messerschmidt, Messersmith (German, Austrian). *A smith who made knives, a cutler.*

Metzger, Metzler (German, Austrian). *A person who sold meat, a butcher.*

Meyer, Meyers, Meier (German, Austrian). *A steward or head servant, also a free farmer.*

Micelli, Micellini (Italian). *See* **Michael.**

Michael, Michaels, Michaelson, Michaelsen, Michaelis (English, Danish, Norwegian, German, Austrian). *Son of Michael, meaning "Who is like unto God?" The Archangel Michael asked this question of Satan who compared himself to God.*

Michal, Michalek, Michalowski, Michalski, Michailoff (Polish, Russian). *See* **Michael.**

Michaud, Michele, Michet (French, Belgian). *See* **Michael.**

Michelangelo (Italian). *A name honoring Michael the Archangel.*

Middleton (English). *The owner of a home in the middle of a village.*

Mihaly (Hungarian). *See* **Michael.**

Miles, Myles (English). *Descendant of a soldier.*

Miller, Millar (English). *A person who ground grain, a miller.*

Mills, Milles (English). A person who lived near a mill.

Milton (English). A person who lived in a mill homestead.

Miranda (Spanish). The wonderful one.

Mitchell (English, Scottish, Irish). See **Michael.**

Molina (Spanish, Italian). The miller who ground flour.

Molnar (Hungarian). See **Molina.**

Molyneaux, Molyneux (French, Belgian). See **Molina.**

Monroe, Monro, Munroe, Munro (Scottish). A person who lived near the red swamp.

Montefiore (Italian, Jewish). A person from Montefiore, meaning "flower mountain."

Montoya (Spanish). A person who lived near the small mountain.

Montgomery, (Welsh, Scottish). A person from the hill of Gomericus in Normandy.

Moody, Moodie (English). The impetuous, brave one.

Mooney (Irish). Descendant of Maonigh, meaning "the wealthy one."

Moore, Moor, More (English, Irish, Scottish). A person who lived on or near the moor; a dark-skinned man.

Morales (Spanish, Portuguese). A person from the place of the blackberry bushes.

Moran (Irish). Son of Morain, meaning "the great young man."

Moreau (French, Belgian). A swarthy, dark-complected man.

Moreno, Moretti (Italian, Spanish). The young, dark-complected man.

Morgan (Welsh). From Mor-can, meaning "sea-bright" or "sea warrior."

Morin (French). The dark-complected man.

Morris (Welsh). A dark-haired, dark-complected man.

Morton (English). A person from Morton, meaning "homestead near the moor."

Moskovitz, Moskowitz (Czechoslovak, Yugoslav, Jewish). A son of Mosko, a form of Moses, meaning a "child saved from the water;" a person from Moscow.

Mosconi (Italian). An active, quick man who reminded people of a fly.

Mueller, Muller (German, Austrian). A person who ground flour, a miller.

Mulvihill (Irish). Grandson of Maolmhichil, a "follower of St. Michael."

Munsen, Monsen, Monson, Manson (Norwegian, Swedish). Son of Mon, a pet form of Magnus, meaning "the great one."

Murphy, Murphey (Irish). Descendant of Murchadha, meaning "the sea warrior."

Murray (Scottish). A man from Moray, meaning "a settlement by the sea."

Myers (German, Austrian). An overseer; a free farmer.

Myles, Miles (English, Welsh). Descendant of Miles, meaning "the soldier."

 *agy* (Hungarian). A big man.

Nash (English). A person who lived near or at the ash tree. The tree was probably a boundary marker.

Navarro, Navarra (Spanish). A person from Navarre, meaning "plain among the hills."

Nelson, Neilson, Nelson, Neilsen (Swedish, Norwegian, Danish, English). Son of Nel or Neil, meaning "the champion."

Nemeth (Hungarian). A man who came from Germany.

Neumann, Neuman, Nieman (German, Austrian, Jewish). A newcomer; a person who performed as a notary; a trustworthy man.

Niarchos (Greek). Descendant of Nearchos, meaning "the new ruler."

Nicholas, Nichols, Nicholson, Nicholl, Nicoll (English, Welsh, Scottish). Son of

Nicholas, meaning "man of the victorious army."

Nicolai, Nicolas, Nicoletti, Nicolo (Norwegian, French, Belgian, Italian). See **Nicholas.**

Nicolopoulos, Nicolopulos (Greek). See **Nicholas.**

Nielsen, Nielson (Danish, Norwegian). Son of Njall or Niel, meaning "the champion."

Nolan, Noland (Irish). A son of Nuall, meaning "famous shout." Possibly a battle cry.

Norman (English, French, Belgian). A man from the north, a Norseman. Later a man from Normandy.

Norris (English). A person from the north; a nurse.

Norton (English). A person whose home was north of the village.

Novak, Novack, Novacek (Czechoslovak, Yugoslav). A stranger or newcomer.

Novotny, Novey (Czechoslovak). A recent newcomer to a community; a foreigner.

Nowak (Polish, Ukrainian). A person from Nowaki, "the new village;" a newcomer to a community.

Nugent (English, Irish). A person from Nogent, or "lush meadow," in France.

berlander (Swiss). A person who lived in the high lands or mountains.

O'Brien, O'Bryan, O'Brian (Irish). Son of Briain. Meaning is obscure. Possibly "hill," "strong," "raven."

O'Connell (Irish). A descendant of Conail, "the high, powerful one."

O'Connor, O'Conners, Connors, Conner (Irish). Descendant of Conchor, meaning "high will" or "high desire;" descendant of Conchobhair, meaning "contentious."

O'Donnell, O'Donell (Irish). Descendant of Domhnaill, meaning "mighty in the world."

O'Hara (Irish). Descendant of Heaghra, "the orderly one."

O'Keefe (Irish). Descendant of Caomh, "the noble, handsome man."

O'Leary (Irish). Descendant of Laoghaire, meaning "the owner of calves."

Oliver, Olivier (English, French, Belgian). A man who tended olive trees.

Olson, Olsen, Olsson (Norwegian, Swedish). Son of Ole or Olaf, an ancient warrior-hero.

O'Malley (Irish). Son of Maille, meaning "the noble chief."

Onassis (Greek). The useful, hard-working man.

O'Neill, O'Neil (Irish). Son of Niall, meaning "the champion."

Oppenheim, Oppenheimer (German, Austrian). A person from Offan-heim, "Offa's home."

O'Reilly, O'Riley (Irish). Son of Raghalligh, "the sportive one," or "the brave warrior."

Orlov, Orloff (Russian). A person with eagle-like qualities.

O'Rourke (Irish). Son of Ruairc (Norse Hrothrekr); "the restless man" or "the high ruler."

Orsini, Orsino (Italian). Son of Orso, meaning "the bear."

Ortega (Spanish). A person who lived at the signboard of the grouse.

Ortiz (Spanish). Son of the spearman.

Osmanski (Polish). Son of the godlike protector; a man who came from Turkey.

Ostrowski (Polish). A person who lived on an island in the river.

Otis (English). Son of Odo, "the rich man."

O'Toole (Irish). Descendant of Tuathail, "the mighty man of the people."

Ott, Otte (German, Austrian). From Otto, meaning "the well-to-do person."

Owens, Owen (Welsh). *Son of Owein, meaning "the well-born one."*

Oxnard (English). *A person who lived near the ford where the oxen crossed the river.*

*abst* (German, Austrian). *A man with a priestlike manner. Probably a man who could read and write.*

Packard (English). *From Bagahard, meaning "powerful in battle."*

Paderewski (Polish). *Son of Patrick meaning "noble, patrician."*

Page, Paige, Padgett, Paget (English). *A young attendant at a medieval court.*

Palmer (English). *A pilgrim who had journeyed to the Holy Land and returned with palm fronds.*

Panos (Greek). *Descendant of Panos, a form of Peter, meaning "the rock;" a form of Panayotis, meaning "follower of Our Lady."*

Papadopoulos, Papadopulos, Pappadopulos (Greek). *The son of a priest.*

Pappas, Papas (Greek). *A priest.*

Parker (English, Welsh). *A gamekeeper in charge of the lord's parks.*

Parson (English). *Son of the parson.*

Patterson, Pattison, Paterson (Scottish, English). *Son of Patrick, meaning "noble, patrician."*

Patton, Patten (English). *Son of young Pat, a shortened form of Patrick meaning "noble, patrician."*

Pauley, Paulsen, Paulson (English, German, Danish, Norwegian, Swedish). *Son of Paul, meaning "the little one."*

Pavel, Pavlov, Pavlovich, Pavlenko (Bulgarian, Romanian, Russian, Ukrainian). *Son of Paul, meaning "the small one."*

Payne, Paine (English). *A farmer or countryman; a pagan.*

Peabody, Peacock (English). *A handsomely-dressed, dandy individual, a peacock.*

Pearson, Pierson (English). *Son of Pier, a pet form of Peter, meaning "the rock."*

Pecora (Italian). *A man who raised and sold sheep.*

Pellegrini (Italian). *A pilgrim from the Holy Land.*

Pelletier, Pellettiere (French, Belgian). *A furrier or a person who dressed furs.*

Pereira (Portuguese). *A person from Pereira, meaning "pear tree."*

Perez (Spanish). *Son of Pero, a pet form of Pedro or Peter, meaning "the rock."*

Perkins, Perkinson (Welsh). *Son of Little Pier, a pet form of Peter, meaning "the rock."*

Perlman (German, Austrian, Jewish). *A dealer in pearls.*

Perrine, Perrin, Perron, Perret, Perreault (French, Belgian). *Descendant of young Pierre or Peter, meaning "the rock."*

Perry (Welsh, English). *A dweller by the pear tree; a descendant of Pier, a form of Peter, meaning "the rock;" a descendant of Perry, a pet form of Peregrine or "the wanderer."*

Peters (English, Welsh). *A descendant of Peter, meaning "the rock."*

Peterson, Petersen (English, Swedish, Danish, Norwegian). *See* **Peters.**

Petrillo, Petrucci, Petrakis, Petros (Italian, Greek). *See* **Peters.**

Petroff, Petrovich, Petrowski, Piotrowski, Petrenko (Russian, Polish, Ukrainian). *See* **Peters.**

Pfeiffer, Pfeifer (German, Austrian). *A musician who played a fife or pipe.*

Pfister (German, Austrian). *A maker of bread, a baker.*

Pfleuger (German, Austrian). *A plowman.*

Philips, Philipps, Phillips (Welsh, English). *Son of Philip, meaning "the lover of horses."*

Picasso (Spanish, Italian). *A man who uses a pick or pickax in his work; a person with the characteristics of a magpie.*

Pierce, Piers (Welsh, English). *Son of Pierce or Piers, early English forms of Peter, meaning "the rock."*

Plamondon (French, Belgian). *A person whose home was built on a level piece of land on a mountainside.*

Podgorny (Polish, Russian). *A person who lived at the foot of the mountain.*

Poe (English). *A person who lived at the signboard of the peacock; a colorfully dressed dandy.*

Pollard (English). *A dweller near a pool; a person who had his hair cropped short.*

Polonsky (Ukrainian). *A captive or prisoner.*

Poole, Pool (English). *A person who lived near a river pool or lake.*

Popescu, Popov, Popoff, Popovic (Romanian, Bulgarian, Russian, Yugoslav, Ukrainian). *Son of the priest.*

Porter (English). *A man who carried goods; a person who tended a gate.*

Powell, Powel (Welsh, English). *Descendant of Powel, a form of Paul, meaning "the small one."*

Powers, Power (English, Irish). *A man who had taken a vow of poverty; a man from de Poers in Normandy.*

Price, Preece (Welsh, English). *From Ap-Rhys, meaning "Son of Rhys." Rhys means "the fiery man" or "the onrushing man."*

Prochaska (Czechoslovak). *A person who traveled by foot.*

Pulaski (Polish). *A family from Pulawy.*

Pulitzer (German, Austrian). *A man who dressed or sold furs, a furrier.*

uigley (Irish). *Descendant of Coigligh, meaning "the wise counselor."*

Quinn (Irish). *Descendant of Cuinn, meaning "the wise one."*

adcliff (English). *A person who lived near the red cliffs.*

Raleigh, Raley, Ralley (English). *A person from Raleigh, meaning "red meadow."*

Ramirez (Spanish). *Son of Ragin-mar, meaning "the mighty counselor."*

Ramsey, Ramsay (English, Scottish). *A person from raven's island or ram's island.*

Randall, Randle, Randell (English). *Descendant of Rand-Wulf, meaning "shield; wolf."*

Rasmussen, Rasmusson (Danish, Norwegian, Swedish). *Forms of Erasmus, meaning "worthy of love."*

Ray, Raye (English). *A pet form of Raymond, meaning "mighty protector;" a person living at the signboard of the roe (red) deer.*

Raymond (English, French, Belgian). *Descendant of Rain-mund, meaning "the mighty protector."*

Reagan, Regan, Ragan (Irish). *Descendant of Riagain, meaning "the young king" or "the impulsive one."*

Rearden, Riordan (Irish). *Descendant of Rioghbhardan, "the king's poet."*

Reed, Reid (English). *A red-haired or ruddy man; a person who lived near the place where the reeds grew.*

Reese, Rees, Reece (Welsh). *Son of Rhys, meaning "the fiery man" or "the onrushing man."*

Reeves (English). *An overseer of the lord's manor.*

Reinhardt, Reinhart, Reinhard (German, Austrian). *Descendant of Raginhart, meaning "powerful counselor."*

Remington (English). *A person from a homestead on the ridge.*

Renard, Reynard (French, Belgian). *Descendant of Raginhart, meaning "powerful counselor;" a person with the qualities of a fox; a person who lived at the signboard of the fox.*

Renaud, Renault (French, Belgian). *Descendant of Raginwalt, meaning "powerful ruler."*

Reyes (Spanish). *A person who played the part of a king in church pageants; a person in a royal household.*

Reynolds (English). *Descendant of Regenweald, meaning "powerful ruler."*

Rhodes, Rhoades, Rhode *(English). A person who lived at the roadside.*

Rice *(Welsh). See* **Reese**.

Richards, Richard *(English, Welsh). Descendant of Richard, meaning "powerful ruler."*

Richenbacker *(German, Austrian). A person from Rickenbach, meaning "the muddy stream."*

Richter, Richters *(German, Austrian). A judge or magistrate.*

Riley *(Irish). Grandson of Raghailligh, meaning "the sportive man."*

Ritter *(German, Austrian). A rider or knight.*

Rivera, Rivero *(Spanish). A dweller near a brook or stream.*

Rizzo, Rizza, Rizzi, Rizzuto *(Italian). A person with wavy or curly hair.*

Roberts, Robertson, Robert, Robart *(Welsh, English). Son of Robert, meaning "bright fame."*

Robinson, Robbins, Robison *(English, Scottish). Son of little Rob, a pet form of Robert, meaning "bright fame."*

Roche *(French, Belgian, Irish, English). A person who lived near a prominent rock, possibly a landmark.*

Rockefeller, Rockenfeller *(German, Austrian). The owner of the rye field.*

Rodriguez, Rodrigues *(Spanish, Portuguese). Son of Rodrigo, a form of Roderick, meaning "famous ruler."*

Rogers, Rogerson, Rodgers *(Welsh, English). Son of Roger, meaning "famous spearman."*

Roget *(French, Belgian). Descendant of Roger, meaning "famous spearman."*

Roland, Rowland, Rowlands *(French, Belgian, English). Son of Hruod-lant, meaning "from the famous land."*

Romano, Romanchek, Romanowski, Romanski *(Italian, Ukrainian, Polish). A person from Rome.*

Romero, Romeo *(Spanish, Italian). A person who made a pilgrimage to Rome.*

Roosevelt *(Dutch). A person who lived near the rose farm or rose field.*

Root *(English). An amiable or cheerful man.*

Rosa *(Spanish, Italian). A man who cultivated roses; a dweller where roses grew; a dweller at the sign of the rose.*

Rosen *(German, Austrian, Dutch, Swedish, Jewish). A person who grew roses; a person who lived at the signboard of the rose.*

Rosenberg, Rosenberger *(German, Austrian, Swiss, Jewish). A person from Rosenberg, "the rose mountain." Most of the many Jewish surnames beginning with "Rose-" honored a beloved ancestress named Rosa, a popular personal name.*

Ross *(Scottish). A person who lived on a promontory.*

Rossi, Rossini, Rossa *(Italian). A red-haired or ruddy-complected man.*

Roth *(German, Austrian). A person with red hair or a ruddy complexion.*

Rothschild *(German, Jewish). The famous family took their name from the red shield on the sign above their door in Frankfurt.*

Roux *(French, Belgian). A person with red or reddish-brown hair or complexion.*

Ruben, Rubin *(German, Austrian, Jewish). A person from the town of Ruben; a descendant of Ruben, meaning "Behold, a son," or "One who renews."*

Rubenstein, Rubinstein *(German, Austrian, Jewish). A ruby or red precious stone; a jeweler's trademark; a person from Rubenstein.*

Rudolph, Rudolf *(German, Austrian). Descendant of Rudolph, meaning "Behold, a son," or "One who renews."*

Ruggiero, Ruggieri *(Italian). Descendant of Ruggiero, a form of Roger, meaning "famous spearman."*

Russell *(English). A little red-haired man.*

Russo *(Italian, Polish). A person with red hair or a red beard; a person from Russia.*

Ryan *(Irish). Son of Riain, meaning "young king."*

Saarinen (Finnish). A person who lived on a ridge or on an island.

Sanchez (Spanish). Son of Sancho, meaning "sanctified."

Sandberg, Sandburg (German, Austrian, Swiss, Swedish). A person who lived near the sandy hill.

Sanders, Saunders (Scottish, English, German, Austrian). Son of Sander, an abbreviation of Alexander, meaning "defender of men."

Sanford (English). A person from Sanford, meaning "sandy ford."

Santiago (Spanish). A person from Santiago, meaning "Saint James."

Santos (Portuguese, Spanish). A person from Dos Santos or Los Santos, meaning "two saints" or "the saints."

Sarkisian, Sarkessian (Armenian). The son of a saint.

Sarnow, Sarnowski (Polish). A person from Sarnowa, "the place of the red deer."

Saroyan (Armenian). A form of Saro Khan, meaning "the mountain prince."

Sauer (German, Austrian). The sower; a sad person.

Schaeffer, Schaefer, Schaffer, Shaffer (German, Austrian, Jewish). A shepherd; a community leader.

Scherer, Scherrer, Schermann (German, Austrian). A shearer of sheep; a barber; a soldier.

Schiller (German, Austrian). A shield-bearer or soldier; a person who squinted.

Schlesinger (German, Austrian, Jewish). A person from Silesia or from Schleusingen.

Schlosser, Schlossman (German, Austrian, Jewish). A locksmith.

Schmidt, Schmitt, Schmitz, Schmit, Schmid (German, Austrian, Dutch). A worker in metals, a blacksmith.

Schneider, Schnieder (German, Austrian, Jewish). A person who made outer garments; a tailor or cloth-cutter.

Schofield (English). A person who lived near the field's storing sheds.

Schreiber, Schriver (German, Austrian). A public or official writer and scribe.

Schreiner (German, Austrian, Jewish). A cabinet-maker.

Schroeder, Schroder, Schrader (German, Austrian). A tailor; a wood-chopper; a drayman.

Schubert, Shubert (German, Austrian, Jewish). A person who made or sold shoes.

Schuler, Schuller, Schueler, Schueller (German, Austrian, Jewish). A teacher or headmaster; a student or scholar.

Schultz, Schulz, Schulze, Schulte, Schultze (German, Austrian). A village mayor or magistrate; an estate steward or overseer.

Schumacher, Shumacher, Schuman (German, Austrian). A person who made or sold shoes.

Schuster, Shuster (German, Austrian). A man who made and repaired shoes.

Schuyler (Dutch). A teacher or schoolmaster.

Schwab, Swope (German, Jewish). A person from Swabia.

Schwartz, Schwarz, Swartz (German, Austrian, Jewish). A dark-haired or dark-complected person.

Schweitzer, Schweizer (German, Austrian). A person who came from Switzerland.

Scott (English). A person from Scotland.

Sears (English). Descendant of Sige-here, meaning "the sea warrior."

Segal (German, Jewish). A farmer who raised rye; an acronym or contraction of segan leviyyan, meaning "member of the Levites."

Seppanen (Finnish). A metal worker or smith.

Shakespeare, Shakespere (English). A person who lived on a farm; a spearman.

Shannon (Irish). Descendant of Seanain, meaning "the wise old man."

Shapiro (German, Austrian, Jewish). A

person from Speyer which was spelled Spiro or Shapira in the Middle Ages.

Shaw, Shawe (Scottish, English). A dweller at the small wood; a descendant of Sithech, meaning "the wolf."

Shea (Irish). Son of Seaghdha, meaning "hawklike" or "stately."

Sheehan, Seahan (Irish). Descendant of young Siodhach, meaning "the peaceful one."

Sheffield (English). A person from Sheffield, meaning "the sheep field."

Shepherd, Shepard, Sheppard (English). A shepherd.

Sheridan (Irish). Descendant of Siridean, "the peaceful one."

Siegal, Siegel (German, Austrian, Jewish). An engraver of seals; victorious young wolf.

Sikorski (Polish, Ukrainian). A person who came from the town Sikora or Sikory, meaning "the titmouse."

Silva, Da Silva, De Silva (Spanish, Portuguese). A person who lived in the forest.

Silverman (German, Austrian, Jewish). A man who made and sold silver articles, a silversmith.

Simmons, Simmonds, Simpson, Simons, Simms (English). Son of Simon, meaning "One who listens intently."

Sinclair (Scottish, English). A person who came from St. Clair in Normandy.

Singer (English, Jewish). A choir singer; a ballad singer; a synagogue cantor.

Sloan, Sloane (Irish). Grandson of Sluaghan, meaning "soldier" or "army man."

Slotnick, Slotnik (Czechoslovak, Russian, Polish). A person who made or sold gold articles, a goldsmith.

Smith, Smyth (English, Scottish, Irish). A worker in metals, a blacksmith.

Snyder, Snider (Dutch). A person who made outer garments, a tailor.

Sobolewski (Polish). A man who trapped sables.

Sokoloff, Sokolov, Sokoloski (Russian, Polish). The son of a man who trained or hunted with hawks or falcons; a dweller at the signboard of the falcon.

Solomon (Jewish, English). Descendant of Solomon, meaning "the peaceful one."

Sorensen, Sorenson, Soren (Danish, Norwegian). Son of Soren, meaning "the severe one."

Southey (English). A person who lived on the south island or near the south stream.

Sousa (Portuguese). A dweller near a salty place or seashore marsh.

Spanos (Greek). A clean-shaven or beardless man.

Spellman, Spelman, Spellmann (German, Austrian, English, Irish). A preacher or orator; a person who entertained by stories, songs or juggling.

Spencer, Spenser (English). A person who dispensed the provisions in a lord's household.

Stanczak, Stankowski, Stankovich, Stanislaus (Polish, Yugoslav, German, Austrian). Forms of Son of Stani-slava, meaning "glorious camp."

Stanley, Standley (English). A person whose home was near the stoney meadow.

Stark, Starke, Starkman (English). A strong, vigorous man.

Stefan, Stefanovich, Stefani, Stefano (Polish, Russian, Yugoslav, Italian). See **Stephens.**

Stein, Steiner, Steins (German, Austrian, Swiss, Jewish). A person whose house was near a large stone or boundary marker; a person who worked in or lived in a stone castle.

Steinberg (German, Austrian, Jewish). A person from Steinberg, meaning "stone mountain."

Steinman (German, Austrian, Jewish). A man who worked in stone, a mason.

Steinmetz (German, Austrian, Jewish). A stone cutter or builder with stone.

Stephanek, Stepanian, Stephani,

Stephano, Stephanos (Polish, Armenian, Italian, Greek). See *Stephens.*

Stephens, Stevens, Stephenson, Stevenson (English, Welsh). Son of Stephen, meaning "the crowned one."

Stern (German, Austrian, Jewish). A person who lived at the signboard of the star. Among Jews, it often represented the Star of David.

Stewart, Steward (English, Scottish). The manager of the household or estate of a king or nobleman.

Stone (English). A person who lived near a large stone or rock, probably a boundary mark.

Strauss (German, Austrian, Jewish). A person who lived near flower shrubbery or at the signboard of the flower bouquet; a person who lived at the signboard of the ostrich.

Strickland (English). A person from Strickland, meaning "the cattle pasture."

Strohmeyer (German, Austrian). A person who was responsible for collecting the tithes of straw for the lord.

Stuyvesant (Dutch). A person from the town of Stuyvesant, meaning "quicksand," in Zeeland.

Sullivan (Irish). Son of Suileabhain. Meaning is obscure. Suil means "eye." Possible meanings: "one-eyed," "dark-eyed," "quick-eyed."

Summerfield, Summerfelt (English, German, Austrian). A dweller near a field used for grazing sheep or cattle in the summer.

Sutton (English). A homestead on the southern outskirts of the village.

Svenson (Swiss). Son of Sven, meaning "young boy" or "servant."

Svoboda, Swoboda (Czechoslovak, Polish, Ukrainian). A lover of freedom; a free man.

Swanson (Swedish). Son of Swayn, meaning "the herder" or "the knight's squire."

Sweeney, Sweeny (Irish). Descendant of Suibhne, meaning "the young hero."

Swift (English). The fleet runner or messenger.

Syzmanski (Polish). Descendant of Szymon, a form of Simon, meaning "One who hearkens."

Szabo (Hungarian). A tailor.

aylor, Tayler (English). A person who made outer garments, a tailor.

Templeton (English). A person from Templeton, an estate of the Knights Templars.

Ten Eyck (Dutch). A person who lived near the oak tree, probably a boundary marker.

Terry (English, Irish). From Theudoric, meaning "ruler of the people;" a son of Terrence, meaning "the tender one."

Thomas, Thompson, Thompsen, Thomasson, Tompkins (English, Scottish, Welsh). Descendant of Thomas, meaning "the twin."

Thoreau (French, Belgian). A man who was as strong as a bull; a descendant of Thore, a pet form of Mathore or Matthew, meaning "gift of God."

Thornton (English). A person from Thornton, a farmstead where thorn-bushes grew.

Tierney, Tiernan (Irish). Descendant of Tighearnaigh, meaning "the lordly one."

Todd (English). A person who lived at the signboard of the fox; a person with fox-like characteristics.

Tolstoy (Russian). The thick-bodied or fat man.

Tomas, Tomasek, Tomaselli, Tomasevich, Tomasian, Tomaszewski, Tomczak (Czechoslovak, Italian, Russian, Armenian, Polish). Son of Thomas, meaning "the twin."

Tonelli (Italian). Son of Anthony, meaning "the peerless one."

Torres, Torre (Spanish, Portuguese). A dweller near a tower or spire; a person who came from Torres.

Toth (Hungarian). *A person who came from Slovakia.*

Townsend (English). *A person who lived at the outskirts of the village.*

Travis (English). *A person who lived at the crossroads.*

Traynor (Irish, English). *Son of Treinfhir, meaning "the strong man;" a man who sets traps.*

Tshaikowsky (Russian). *A person from Tschaykovo, meaning "a place frequented by lapwings."*

Trudeau (French, Belgian). *From the matronym Gertrude, meaning "strong spear."*

Tucker (English). *A person who cleaned and thickened cloth.*

Turek (Polish, Czechoslovak). *A man who came from Turkey.*

Turner (English). *A carpenter who fashioned objects on a lathe.*

Ullman, Ullmann, Ulman (German, Austrian). *A person who owned land; a person from Ulm, meaning "the bog."* **Ulrich, Ullrich, Ulrick** (German, Austrian). *Descendant of Ulrich, meaning "the powerful, rich man."*

Underwood (English). *A person who lived at the edge of a wood.*

Urbanski (Polish). *Descendant of Urban, "the town dweller."*

Urquhart (Scottish). *A person who came from Urquhart, meaning "in the wood."*

Urso (Italian). *A person who lived at the signboard of the bear; a man who possessed bearlike strength.*

Valdez, Valdes (Spanish). *Son of the prince; a person from Valdes, meaning "tableland."* **Van Buren** (Dutch). *A person from Buren, meaning "a place of buildings."*

Vanderbilt (Dutch). *A person whose home was near an earth mound.*

Vandermeer (Dutch). *A person who lived near the lake.*

Van Dyke, Vandyck, Van Dyk (Dutch). *A person who lived near the dike.*

Van Horn (Dutch). *A person from Hoorn, meaning "a promontory."*

Varga (Hungarian). *A shoemaker or cobbler.*

Vargas (Spanish, Portuguese). *A person from Vargas, meaning "the steep hillside."*

Vartanian, Vardanian (Armenian). *Descendant of Vartan, meaning " a follower of the savior."*

Vasilauskos, Vasilauskas, Vasilescu, Vasilevich, Vasilenko, Vasilevsky (Greek, Lithuanian, Romanian, Russian, Ukrainian). *Son of Vasil. Vasil or Basil means "kingly."*

Vasques (Spanish). *A Basque; a shepherd; a person living at the signboard of the raven.*

Vaughan, Vaughn (Welsh, Irish). *Son of Vychan, meaning "the short one;" son of Machain, meaning "the first one."*

Velasques, Velazquez (Spanish). *Son of the Basque; son of the stammerer; son of Bela, meaning "the raven." The raven symbolized wisdom.*

Venuti, Venuto (Italian). *Descendant of Venuto, a shortened form of Benevenuto, meaning "the welcome one."*

Verne, Vernon (French, Belgian, English). *A person who lived near the alder grove.*

Villar, Villars, Villard, Villiers (French, Belgian). *A person who lived in a country house or village.*

Vitale, Vitali (Italian). *A lively, vital person.*

Vlahos (Greek). *A shepherd.*

Vogel, Vogl (German, Austrian, Dutch). *A person whose shop-sign pictured a bird; a sprightly person who reminded people of a bird.*

Vogt, Voight, Voigt (German, Austrian).

The manager or steward of a nobleman's household.

Volkman, Volkmann (German, Austrian). Descendant of Fole-man, meaning "servant of the people."

Voroshilov (Russian). A restless, active man.

Voss (Dutch, German, Austrian). A person who lived at the signboard of the fox; a person with red hair or fox-like characteristics.

**ade** (English, Irish). A person who lived at the river crossing; a son of the yellow-haired man.

Wagner, Waggoner, Wagoner (English, German, Austrian). A wagon-driver or wagon maker.

Walbridge (English). A person who lived near a bridge at the Roman wall.

Walcott (English). A person who lived in a stone-walled cottage.

Waldorf (German, Austrian). A person from Waldorf, meaning "swampy village."

Walensa (Polish). The rover or the wanderer.

Walker (English). A cloth-worker who cleaned and thickened dampened wool by treading on it.

Wallace, Wallis (Scottish). A man from Wales; a foreigner.

Walsh, Walshe (English, Irish). A person from Wales; a foreigner.

Walters (Welsh, English). Descendant of Walter, meaning "powerful warrior" or "army ruler."

Walton (English). A person who lived in a home with stone walls; a person who lived near the fortress wall.

Ward, Warden, Warder (English). A guard; a gamekeeper; a watchman.

Warner, Warren, Warrin (English). A keeper of a game preserve; a descendant of Warren, meaning "protection;" a person living near or tending the rabbit hutch.

Washington (English). A person from the homestead of the wise man's family. Derived from the Old English Hwaes-ing-tun. Hwaes means "wise man," -ing means "family", -tun means "homestead."

Watson, Watts, Watt, Watkins (English). A son of Wat, a pet form of Walter, meaning "powerful warrior" or "army ruler."

Weaver (English). A weaver of cloth.

Weber, Webb (English, German, Austrian, Jewish). A weaver of cloth.

Weinstein (German, Austrian, Jewish). A person who lived near Weinstein, meaning "wine mountain."

Weiss, Weis (German, Austrian, Jewish). A person with light hair or white hair; a wise man; a person from the town of Weiss or Weis.

Welch, Welsh (English). A person from Wales.

Wellington (English). A person from Wellington, a village or homestead near a well or spring.

Wells, Welles (English). A person living near a spring or well.

West (English). A person from the west country.

Whalen (Irish). Descendant of Faolan, meaning "the little wolf."

Wheeler (English). A person who made wheels and wagons.

White (English). A light or fair-complected person; a person with white hair.

Whitfield (English). A person who came from Whitfield or "the white field."

Wiener (Austrian). A person from Vienna. The name of Austria's capital city was derived from the Slavic word "vindobna" meaning "white fortress."

Wilcox, Williams, Wilkins, Wilkinson (English). Son of little Will, a pet form of William, meaning "resolution; helmet." Usually translated as "resolute protector."

Wilhelm, Willem (German, Austrian). Descendant of Wilhelm, meaning "resolution; helmet." Usually Wilhelm is translated as "resolute protector."

Williams, Williamson, Wills, Will (English, Welsh). Son of William, meaning "resolution; helmet." Usually translated as "resolute protector."

Willis, Willison (English). See *Williams.*

Wilson (English, Scottish). See *Williams.*

Wirtz, Wirz (German, Austrian). A host or owner of a tavern or inn.

Wisniewski (Polish). A person who came from the town of Wizsnia, meaning "cherry tree."

Wolf, Wolfe, Wolff (English, German, Austrian, Jewish). A man with the fighting qualities of a wolf; a dweller at the signboard of the wolf. Among Jews the wolf symbolized the Israelite tribe of Benjamin.

Wolfgang (German, Austrian). Descendant of Wolfgang, meaning "wolf path."

Wood, Woods (English). A person living in or near a forest.

Wright (English). A man who worked in wood; a wagon-maker; a wheel-maker; a carpenter.

Wulf, Wulff (German, Austrian, Jewish). See *Wolf.*

 *ablon, Yablonski, Yablonsky* (Polish). A person living near an apple orchard or an apple tree which was a boundary marker.

Yaeger (German, Austrian). A lord's huntsman.

Yates, Yeats (English, Irish). A person who lived near the gate; a gatekeeper.

Young, Younger, Younge, Jung (English, German, Austrian). The younger son; a man younger than those with whom he was associated.

 *acharias* (Greek). Zacharias is a form of Zacariah, meaning "One whom God remembers."

Zahn (German, Austrian). A person who lived near the pointed rock, probably a boundary marker.

Zalewski (Polish). A person who lived near the flooded place or the swamp.

Zeiss (German, Austrian). A genial and gracious man.

Zhukov (Russian). A person who lived at the signboard of the beetle or the scarab.

Ziegfeld (German, Austrian). A person who lived near a field where goats were kept.

Ziegler, Zeigler (German, Austrian, Jewish). A maker of roofing tiles.

Zimmerman, Zimmer, Zimmermann (German, Austrian, Jewish). A carpenter.

Zuckerman, Zucker (German, Austrian, Jewish). A person who sold sugar.

Zumwalt (German, Austrian, Jewish). A person who lived in or near the forest.

Recommended Reading on the Subject of Surnames

You'll find many of these excellent books in better bookstores. If they do not have them in stock, they will order those volumes for you which are still in print. Public libraries are probably your best source for most of these volumes. If the book you're seeking is not on the shelves, they might be able to obtain it for you through the inter-library loan service.

A Dictionary of Jewish Names and Their History by Benzion C. Kaganoff, Schocken Books, New York, 1977.

A Guide to the Origins of British Surnames by Cecil L'Estrange Ewen, London, 1938.

An Introduction to Polish Surnames by R. A. Bolesta-Kozlowski, Toronto, Ontario, 1972.

A Treasury of Name Lore by Elsdon C. Smith, Harper and Row, New York, 1967.

Black Names in America by Newbell Niles Puckett, G. R. Hall & Co., Boston, 1975.

British Family Names by Charles Wareing Bardsley, London, 1902.

Deutsches Namen-Lexicon by Hans Bahlow, Keyeresche, Munich, Germany, 1967.

Dictionnaire Etymologiques des Noms de Famille et Prenoms de France by Albert Dauzat, Larousse, Paris, 1951.

English Surnames, Their Sources and Significations by Charles Wareing Bardsley, Charles E. Tuttle Co., Rutland, Vermont, 1968.

Family Names and Their Story by S. Baring-Gould, Seeley & Co., Ltd., London, 1910.

International Book of Names by C. O. Sylvester Mawson, Thomas J. Crowell Company, New York, 1934.

Irish Families, The Names, Arms and Origins by Edward MacLysaght, Crown Publishers, New York, 1972.

Irish Names and Surnames by Patrick Woulfe, Genealogical Publishing Co., Baltimore, Maryland, 1923.

New Dictionary of American Family Names by Elsdon C. Smith, Harper and Row, New York, 1973.

Niederdeutsches Namenbuchen by Hans Bahlow, Wolluf bei Wiesbaden, 1972.

Our Family Names, Where They Came From and What They Mean by Eloise Lambert and Mario Pei, Lothrop, Lee and Shepard, Inc., New York, 1968.

Our Italian Surnames by Joseph G. Fucilla, Evanston, Illinois, 1949.

Russian Surnames by B. O. Ungelbaum, Clarendon Press, Oxford, 1972.

Surnames of the United States by Henry Harrison, Genealogical Publishing Co., Baltimore, Maryland, 1969.

These Names of Ours by Augustus Wilfred Dellquist, New York, 1938.

The Story of Our Names by Elsdon C. Smith, Harper and Brothers, New York, 1950.

The Story of Surnames by Lester G. Pine, Charles E. Tuttle Co., Rutland, Vermont, 1967.

The Surnames of Ireland by Edward MacLysaght, Irish Academic Press, Dublin, 1978.

What's in a Name, Surnames of America by La Reine Rule and William K. Hammond, Jove Publications (Harcourt Brace Jovanovich), New York, 1977.

What's Your Name? by Louis Adamic, Harper and Brothers Publishers, New York, 1942.

Your Book of Surnames by Pennethorne Hughes, Faber and Faber, London, 1967.

The Names of Our Family and Friends

On these pages you can record the meanings of your family names and the names of your friends and associates. If you are unable to find the definition of a name in the preceding chapters, we suggest that you refer to the guide books and surname dictionaries listed in the Bibliography on page 196.

Husband's Family

RELATIONSHIP TO HUSBAND	SURNAME OR MAIDEN NAME	MEANING OF NAME
Father		
Mother		
Paternal Grandmother		
Maternal Grandfather		
Maternal Grandmother		
Uncle		
Uncle		
Aunt		
Aunt		
Brother-in-Law		
Brother-in-Law		
Sister-in-Law		
Sister-in-Law		

Wife's Family

RELATIONSHIP TO WIFE	SURNAME OR MAIDEN NAME	MEANING OF NAME
Father		
Mother		
Paternal Grandmother		
Maternal Grandfather		
Maternal Grandmother		
Uncle		
Uncle		
Aunt		
Aunt		
Brother-in-Law		
Brother-in-Law		
Sister-in-Law		
Sister-in-Law		

Our Friends

SURNAME OR MAIDEN NAME	MEANING OF NAME

Heraldry and Coats of Arms

For most of us, the chivalry of the Middle Ages and the romance of the Renaissance are symbolized in the pageantry of heraldry with its colorful shields, lordly helmets, rampant lions and fascinating crests. In truth, heraldry is a meaningful and decorative art form which has been dramatized and enriched by our memories of King Arthur and the Knights of the Round Table, Ivanhoe, Robin Hood, Richard the Lionhearted and all the kings and queens, lords and ladies of history.

Although we thoroughly enjoy heraldry and its handsome coats of arms, many of us feel that, in this country, there is something alien and pretentious about it. Perhaps reading this chapter will bring a new understanding and perspective to this time-honored subject.

Among the mistaken ideas about coats of arms is the belief that they are the sacred emblems of the blue-blooded members of the royal and noble families of Europe. It is true that these families and their descendants have the right to display their own distinctive symbols, but it is also true that millions of people in America do not realize that they too have inherited ancient family coats which they have the privilege of displaying in a fitting manner.

It should be remembered that the granting of coats of arms (usually called "arms") was not restricted to the aristocracy. The majority of arms were granted to people of gentle blood or to citizens who had distinguished themselves in some noteworthy way. For instance, in the 16th century more than one thousand proud citizens in a small German city had their own individual coats of arms. Just think how many untold thousands were granted throughout the hundreds of European kingdoms, principalities, cities and dioceses during the past centuries. And they continue to be granted today, as witnessed by the fact that the College of Arms in England has registered more coats of arms in this century than it has during its entire history.

The Traditions of Heraldry

The guiding rules of heraldry vary from country to country. In England it is held that a coat of arms can be used only by a direct descendant of the man who was originally granted the arms. In Ireland, on the other hand, it is believed that if there is a coat of arms registered in your rightful name, you are privileged to use that coat of arms. Probably this theory is based on the fact that Irish people with the same ancient family name are related in some way through blood, marriage, adoption or clan relationship. The traditions of heraldry varied throughout the countries of Europe, from Spain to Russia and from Italy to Scandinavia.

Most people are under the impression that their rights to display a coat of arms are limited to the surname they bear. Happily this is not true. You can use the coats of arms of any of your ancestors and ancestresses who were entitled to arms. If you glance at your Family Tree Chart, you'll see that you've had thirty-two ancestors and ancestresses in just the past five generations, sixty-four in the past six generations, etc. If any of them had the right to a coat of arms, you have probably inherited that right.

Heraldry in the Twentieth Century

Today the value and purpose of a coat of arms is sometimes questioned. Is it an example of exclusivity and snobbery? Is having a coat of arms or a pedigree (family tree) an attempt to prove that one person is superior to another because he can trace his lineage to more distant or distinguished ancestors?

It is true that in the past some newly-rich people hoped to become "socially acceptable" by desperately trying to establish an aristocratic family lineage. However few people today are tracing their families' trees for such purposes. After all, as we've pointed out, millions of us have the right to our family coats of arms, and all of us have pedigrees if we have the initiative to trace and record them. So there is nothing exclusive or particularly praiseworthy about having a coat of arms or a pedigree.

However, in this writer's opinion, they can be of great value within the privacy of one's family. Coats of arms and family trees are the symbols and the written records which document the unique and continuing existence of a family in history. They can strengthen the bonds of unity and pride within a family. And among its younger members, they bring a challenging new perspective to their lives, a new awareness of being indispensable parts in something worthwhile and enduring. In our troubled and uncertain times, these are indeed matters of value.

In a lighter vein, it must be admitted that it is reassuring and pleasant to know that, among one's hundreds of ancestors, there were a few men and women who, through courage, birth, loyal service, marriage, integrity, business acumen, luck or skullduggery were honored with a coat of arms.

Although some upholders of traditional heraldry might object, we can understand why some families are designing their own coats of arms. If it's done in good taste and dignity, and if it displays the symbols of one's family heritage, origins and achievements, such a coat of arms with an appropriate motto may accomplish the worthwhile purposes outlined above. We all have the right to be proud of our families and our heritage.

The story of heraldry is an intriguing one. As a traditional art and as a means of communication, it played a continuing role of great importance in the lives of our ancestors and in the history of Europe. The books which have been written about heraldry would fill libraries, so the following pages should be considered as a brief introduction to a highly complex subject.

The Beginnings of Heraldry

We read in Homer's **Iliad** that the great Greek and Trojan heroes were identified in battle by their distinctive helmets, breastplates, shields and weapons. However it was not until the 12th century that men of high birth formally adopted heraldic designs and symbols which were both unique and hereditary to their families.

Instant recognition of military leaders in combat became essential when noblemen and knights encased themselves in iron armor from head to foot. In the wild turmoil of battle, it was vital that men-at-arms be able to recognize their leader immediately, because he was their rallying point and the man who led their charges, maneuvers and retreats.

It is noteworthy that heraldry developed simultaneously with the Crusades and with the spread of hereditary surnames during the Middle Ages. Noblemen had their own personal insignia and designs painted on their shields and embroidered on the cloth surcoats worn over their armor. Hence the expression "coat of arms" or simply "arms." Coats of arms were displayed on banners, trappings of horses, tapestries, furniture, signet rings, seals and everything of value, military and nonmilitary, which the noblemen owned. They were usually depicted within the shape of the traditional shield which in heraldry is called an escutheon.

To avoid duplication and confusion, noblemen came to rely on professional heralds whose duties were to record and authenticate not only coats of arms, but titles of nobility, rights of inheritance, succession and other genealogical matters. Heraldry at this point became more than a means of battlefield identification.

The quick recognition and continuity afforded by coats of arms had many benefits in an age of illiteracy, so their use became widespread, not only for the nobility, knights and high churchmen, but also for nations, provinces, counties, cities, cathedrals, dioceses, universities, guilds, etc.

The Blazon of a Coat of Arms

The heraldic **achievement** usually consists of six elements. From the top to the bottom, they are the **crest, helmet, wreathe, mantling, coat of arms, supporters** and **motto** or scroll. The all-important element, of course, is the coat of arms.

When a coat of arms is described in proper heraldic terms, it is called a **blazon**. A coat of arms consists of two parts, the **field** (background) of the shield and the **charges** (designs and symbols) placed on the field. The blazon first describes the **tincture** or color of the field. The names of tinctures, like all heraldic terms, are a mixture of Old English and Norman French.

The tinctures are named **gules** for red, **azure** for blue, **vert** for green, **sable** for black, **purpure** for purple, **sanguine** for blood red, **or** for gold, **argent** for silver or white, **proper** for natural color or flesh color. There are also several fur tinctures including **ermine** (a white background with black spots of various shapes), **ermines** (a black background with white spots of various shapes), **erminois** (a gold background

with black spots), **vair** (alternating shield-shapes of blue and white) and several others.

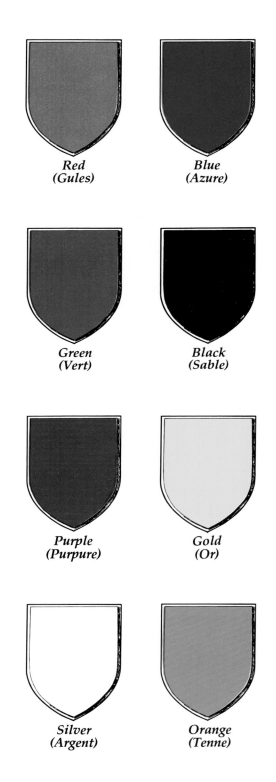

Heraldic Colors
Heraldic names appear in parenthesis.

Red
(Gules)

Blue
(Azure)

Green
(Vert)

Black
(Sable)

Purple
(Purpure)

Gold
(Or)

Silver
(Argent)

Orange
(Tenne)

Ermine

Ermines

Quartered

Per pale

Vair

Per fess

Per bend

Per bend sinister

Per bend

The right side of the shield or escutcheon from the bearer's point of view (not the observer's) is called the **dexter** side, and the left side is called the **sinister** side. Sinister means "left" in Latin, so the word does not have ominous implications.

Ordinaries are broad bands or areas of color. A band across the top of a shield is called a **chief**. The **fess** is a horizontal band; the **pale** is a vertical band; the **cross** is a combined **fess** and **pale** (forming an upright cross); the **saltire** is a diagonal cross in the form of a large X; the **pall** is a big Y extending to the shield's three points; a **lozenge** is a large diamond area; the **chevron** points upward like a large inverted V; the **pile** is a triangular wedge shape pointing downward like a V.

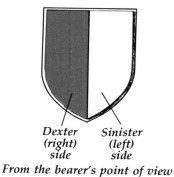

Dexter (right) side   Sinister (left) side

From the bearer's point of view

When a shield is divided horizontally and vertically into quadrants, it is said to be **quartered**. When it is divided vertically, it is described as **per pale**; horizontally, **per fess**; diagonally from dexter to sinister, **per bend**; diagonally from sinister to dexter, **per bend sinister**.

Chief

Fess

Pale

Cross

Saltire

Pall

Lozenge

Chevron

Pile

Heraldic Symbols

Most of us find the heraldic symbols to be the most interesting charges placed on the escutcheon. Incidently, the charges are considered to be three-dimensional, as if they were pieces of metal welded to the field of the shield. Many symbols are thought-provoking because they represent some virtue, deed or event in the lives of the original bearer or his family.

The meanings of the various symbols were not universal, but the ones listed below are accepted by many heraldists:

When charges were used as symbols, they represented some virtue, deed or events in the lives of the original bearer or his family. Most heraldists agree on these meanings:

Bear–great strength or protection
Bull–courage and determination
Castle–solidity and strength
Chevron–reward for achievement
Cross–religious devotion or Crusade
Cross bar–self-control and steadfastness
Dolphin–charity or kindness
Dove–peace and religious faith
Eagle–royalty or high ideals
Falcon or Hawk–eagerness or elan in battle
Fleur-de-lis–French royalty or allied lineages
Fox–wisdom or cleverness
Gauntlet–vanquished enemies
Goat–practical wisdom or prudence
Griffin–valor in battle
Hound–loyalty or great courage
Heart–sincerity
Lamb–devotion to Christianity
Lion–nobility, courage, power
Oak tree–strength or endurance
Olive branch–peace
Owl–wisdom
Pelican–Christianity
Raven–wisdom
Ring–fidelity
Rooster–pride and courage
Seashell–pilgrimage or Crusade
Ship–achievement in naval warfare
Spear–achievement in war
Stag–strength, harmony or peace
Triangle–unity
Vertical stripe–uprightness of character
Wavy lines–rivers or oceans
Wolf–valiant in battle

Bear

Bull

Castle

Chevron

Griffin

Hound

Cross

Cross bar

Heart

Lamb

Dolphin

Dove

Lion

Oak tree

Eagle

Falcon or Hawk

Olive branch

Owl

Fleur-de-lis

Fox

Pelican

Raven

Gauntlet

Goat

Ring

Rooster

Seashells

Ship

Spear

Stag

Triangle

Vertical stripe

Wavy lines

Wolf

Heraldic terms are precise when describing a charge. An animal is **rampant** when standing on its hind legs and pawing the air. It is **statant** when standing on its four feet and **passant** when walking. If it is looking at you, it is **guardant** unless it's a stag which is **at gaze.** When an animal is sitting, it is **sejant,** and it is **vorant** when eating. **Embowed** means arched and usually refers to its neck or back.

If a bird's wings are spread and the tips are pointed upward, it is **displayed.** If the tips are pointed downward, it is **displayed and inverted.** When its wings are down, the bird is **closed,** and when it is flying, it is **volant.**

Armed refers to an animal's claws, tusks and hooves, or to a bird's beak or talons. **Langued** refers to the tongue. These two terms are often used when describing tinctures, as "Langued gules" meaning "with red tongue."

When the head or limb of an animal or bird is used as a charge, **couped** means that it has been cut off cleanly, and **erased** means that it has a jagged edge. **Demi-** means halved.

Among the many inanimate charges are the sun, moon, stars, castles, towers, portcullises, ships, trees, bushes, flowers, and a wide array of geometric shapes.

Sons, Daughters and Wives

According to the strictest rules of heraldry, only one person had the right to bear his family's coat of arms. However the sons of an arms-bearing father could display the family coat of arms by adding charges called **marks of cadency** to their escutcheons.

The mark of cadency for the eldest son was called a **Label.** This device consisted of three short vertical bars topped by a long horizontal bar. For the second son, the mark was a **Crescent** (with its tips pointed upward); for the third son, a **Mullet** (a star); for the fourth son, a **Martlet** (a bird without feet); for the fifth son, an **Annulet** (a ring); for the sixth son, a **Fleur-de-lys;** for the seventh son, a **Rose;** for the eighth son, a **Cross Moline** (a cross whose four ends were forked); the ninth son, a **Double Quarterfoil** (a flower with eight petals). It seems that the heralds were ready to accommodate large families.

On the death of the father, the eldest son inherited the family coat of arms and removed the Label from his escutcheon. The other sons (no longer heirs) changed their shield by adding or eliminating charges, tinctures and borders, while still retaining a strong family resemblance to the original.

Coats of arms were not confined to the masculine members of the family. Daughters were permitted to display their father's arms within an elongated diamond shape called a **lozenge.** When a daughter married, she placed her family coat of arms next to her husband's on the escutcheon. Her coat was on the sinister (left) half of the shield, and his were on the dexter (right) half. This was called impaling.

If a father died without a male heir, his eldest daughter became an heraldic heiress, a title having nothing to do with money or property. If she married, her family coat of arms (half-size) was placed in the center of her husband's coat of arms, which was called an **inescutcheon of pretence.** Their children's coats of arms would then be quartered. The shield would be divided into four equal quadrants, upon which the arms of both of their parents appeared.

If there are further generations of heraldic heiresses, their coats of arms are fitted into these quadrants. At this point, heraldry becomes even more complicated, and if you are interested in further pursuing this subject, we suggest you consult any of the books listed at the end of this chapter.

7th Son — Rose

8th Son — Cross Moline

9th Son — Double Quarter foil

Lozenge

1 Son — Label

2nd Son — Crescent

3rd Son — Mullet

4th Son — Martlet

5th Son — Annulet

6th Son — Fleur-de-lys

Recommended Books on Heraldry for Your Further Study

A Complete Guide to Heraldry by Arthur Charles Fox-Davies, T. C. and E. C. Jack, Ltd., London, 1925.

Fairbairn's Book of Crests of the Families of Great Britain and Ireland by James Fairbairn, Genealogical Publishing Co., Baltimore, Maryland, 1968.

Heraldry Explained by Arthur Charles Fox-Davies, Charles E. Tuttle Company, Rutland, Vermont, 1971.

Intelligible Heraldry by Sir Christopher Lynch-Robinson and Adrian Lynch-Robinson, Heraldic Book Company, Baltimore, Maryland, 1967.

International Heraldry by Leslie G. Pine, David and Charles, Newton Abbot, England, 1970.

Shield and Crest by Julian Franklyn, Genealogical Publishing Co., Baltimore, Maryland, 1967.

Simple Heraldry by Iain Moncreiffe and Don Pettinger, Thomas Nelson and Sons, Ltd., London, 1953.

The Nature of Arms by Lt. Col. Robert Gayre, Oliver and Boyd, London, 1961.

The Symbols of Artistry Explained, Heraldic Artists, Ltd., Dublin, 1980.

The Full Achievement

As we have pointed out, there are usually six elements in a complete heraldic achievement.

Mounted on top of the escutcheon or shield is a **helmet** upon which rests a **wreath** of rolled silk whose purpose (in real life) was to hold in place a **mantling** or flowing cape which draped down the wearer's back to shield his armor from the heat of the sun. On top of the helmet is a **crest** which is a plume, animal, bird or any other device. Its purpose was to further distinguish the bearer from other helmeted warriors in the confusion of battle.

On both sides of the escutcheon are **supporters** which can be upright animals, human figures, trees, pillars or anything decorative and appropriate. Then a scroll or scrolls bearing the motto of the individual or his family completes the **full** achievement, the glorious triumph of heraldry.

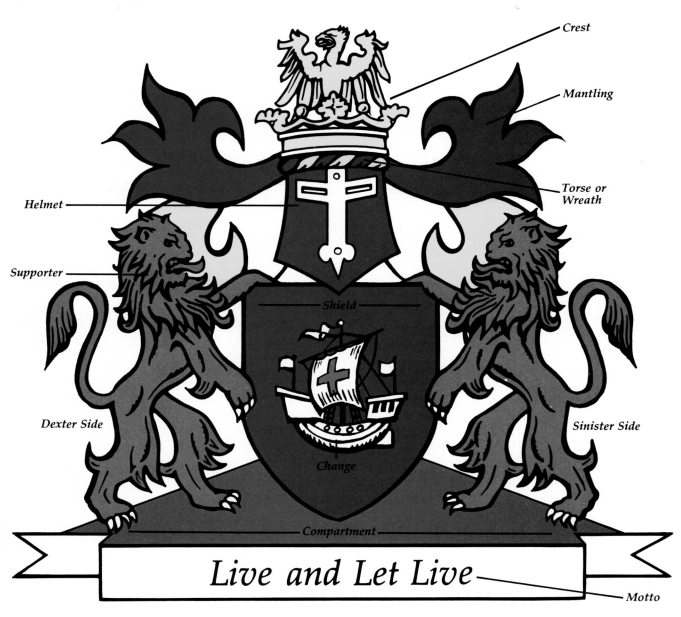

Crest

Mantling

Torse or Wreath

Helmet

Supporter

Dexter Side

Shield

Change

Sinister Side

Compartment

Live and Let Live

Motto

Some Thoughts Before Naming a Baby

 ne of the highlights in the life of every mother and father is that memorable moment when they select "the perfect name" for their newborn baby. Before reaching this happy moment, most parents have spent weeks discussing and pondering the merits of a dozen or more likely names which they've finally narrowed down to three or four favorites. If a mother and father have arrived at this point in their search, it's possible that reading this chapter might help them make a choice which will be a happy one for their child.

First of all, there should be only one question in the minds of parents when choosing a name for their child. Will the name they are considering be a continuing source of happiness, support and pride for their child throughout the years of its life?

This straightforward question makes clear the responsibility of both parents to their child and its future. If they accept this responsibility, and if they exercise common sense and good taste, they can be confident that they will choose "the perfect name" for their baby during its childhood and its future years as a teen-ager, young adult and mature individual.

Mothers and fathers have always believed that the lives of their children would be strongly influenced by the names which were given to them. Our primitive ancestors named their children with great care in order to win the protection of friendly gods and to ward off evil spirits. In later centu-ries, Jewish names became reverent prayers to Jehovah, and Christian children were given the names of saints to serve as spiritual models for them to follow.

Through the ages, people have sensed that each name possessed a sort of magic of its own. Today we would probably use the word "personality" rather than magic.

The Personalities of Names

Research studies are confirming that there is a high level of agreement among people regarding the personalities which they associate with specific given names. Surveys also indicate that people generally expect that individuals will be the type of person associated with his or her name.

They readily place feminine names in such classifications as Lovely, Charming, Aristocratic, Successful, Energetic, Vivacious, Sensuous, Sexy, Wholesome, Unpopular, Silly, Passive, Dull. Masculine names are also given descriptive designations such as Extremely Manly, Born Leader, Strong, Successful, Energetic, Sophisticated, Trustworthy, Imaginative, Likeable, Conservative, So-so, Ineffective, Effeminate.

Probably your perceptions of individual names would agree with the majority of people. However all of us have personal reasons for being fond of some names which most people thoroughly dislike. Before giving such a name to a child, parents should consider some of the possible results which we will discuss.

PreConceived Ideas About Names

As we've suggested, people subconsciously assume that we are going to be the type of person they associate with our names. You've probably heard someone say, "She isn't at all like her name," or "He fits his name perfectly." This general tendency to judge people by their names extends to our working lives where research indicates that men and women with positive names are generally promoted more quickly than people with peculiar or negative names.

They also find it easier to get jobs, according to employment agency managers. One of them stated bluntly, "Put yourself in the position of a busy executive who only has time to interview two applicants for a responsible position. Let's say I send you the applications of three qualified men named Egbert, Daniel and Stephen. Be honest. Who are the two men you'd interview? If a position calls for a dynamic saleslady, and I send you the applications of Susan, Esmeralda and Barbara, who are the two ladies you would find time to talk to?"

Name-awareness begins early in life. Surveys among school children indicate that popular girls and boys tend to have well-liked names. Perhaps their classmates accept them more readily because they like their names. Or perhaps children with well-liked names are more at ease with themselves and are therefore more outgoing and pleasant to be with.

This example introduces a highly important consideration for parents who are selecting a name for their child. There is mounting evidence that an individual's name can exert strong influences on his own self-image and his conception of his capacities. If a person's name has positive and desirable associations, he tends to gain confidence and to attempt to fulfill the promise of his name. To cite one convincing example: analyses of scholastic records show that male and female students with positive names usually perform better and receive a higher level of grades than students with peculiar or negative names.

The Crucial Early Years

Never before have we been made so aware that a child's early years are the all-important formative period in determining its future character and personality. We read this clear message in our books and newspapers, and we hear it on TV and radio.

Yet almost every day we observe how some parents have selected a name for their child for the evident purpose of showing how witty or imaginative or daring they are. They fail to realize that a name that is peculiar, bizarre or negative will make a child or a teenager the object of the derision and jokes of its peers, and that suffering such continuing humiliation can make a child timid, self-conscious and apologetic, or defensive, bitter and withdrawn.

Names which are considered to be unmanly or sissified can be a particularly heavy burden for a boy to bear. Although some boys can overcome such an unnecessary handicap, it is difficult to think of a valid reason for calling a boy Percival, Cuthbert or any of the other names which have also become the targets of prejudice in recent years.

Girls also suffer embarrassment when parents, in the desire to be "different," give them names which are considered ridiculous or overly pretentious by their peers. It is true that youngsters are lenient in accepting girl's names which are unusual and daring, but they can be cruel to a newcomer whose name they find downright silly or objectionable. Iolantha, Ludmilla and Thisbe are time-honored names, but parents giving these names to their children are not doing them a favor.

Young people are intrigued with one another's names. They play games with the initials and sounds, make up silly rhymes, add syllables and interpret meanings into names which were never intended. It is difficult for parents to foresee these eventualities, but they should think about the nicknaming

possibilities of names like Sheldon Bell and Shelley Bell becoming Shelley Belly, or the unfortunate initials of a Frances Anne Thompson (FAT) and a Samuel Arthur Perkins (SAP).

Pronunciation and Spelling

One of the primary requirements of a name is that it should be easy for other people to pronounce and to spell. Names which violate this rule can be a source of irritation both for their bearers and for the people with whom they come in contact. Classmates, teachers, acquaintances and business associates find it annoying to try to remember how what's-her-name wants her name to be pronounced.

A classic example is a girl named Alysse who said that she was addressed (usually in mumbles) as Al-eyes, Al-ease, All-ease, Al-easy, Al-ice, Alice, etc. She also found that her name was misspelled as often as it was spelled correctly. Names with peculiar and awkward letter arrangements can cause troublesome errors in the recording and filing of one's scholastic, employment and official records.

However, changes can be made in spelling which do not cause these problems, but which create distinctive new name personalities: Patti, Toni, Betti, Bette, Kathryn, Barbra, Carlyn, Deanna, Faythe, Robyn, Gayle, Ellyn, Lynda, Maggi, Carolyn, Madelyn, Helaine, Kathlyne.

Nicknames and Parental Names

It is gratifying to learn that most normal nicknames (Dave, Matt, Patty, Beth) have positive associations which are as strong or stronger than the given names from which they were derived. This is not surprising in our nickname-loving society. In many cases, it seems advisable to give the full names to children and thus allow them to make their own choice. If a boy is named John rather than Jack, he can decide for himself whether he wants to be called John, Johnny or Jack. Katherine can pick Kay, Kathy, Kate, Kathie, Kitty or Kit as she desires. As in all naming procedures, this is a matter of parental discretion.

Many psychologists feel that giving a father's full name to his son can place undue pressure on the boy to emulate his father rather than develop his own future and his own individuality. They believe that being called "Junior" is unfair and implies that the son might be unable to earn respect and success on his own merits. In some instances, there are good reasons for not following this precept. A satisfactory alternative is to give the father's first name to the son as a middle name. This establishes a special bond between the two, and the son can use the middle name as he sees fit.

The Nationalities of Given Names

In the past, parents have been advised not to choose given names for their children which differed in national origin from their surnames. It is true that some combinations of names with varying nationality backgrounds produce surprising affects, such as Hildegard Garibaldi, Dmitri O'Brien, Carmelita Swenson and Desdemona Schultz.

On the other hand, it is clear that names of differing nationalities can be combined with pleasing results: Brian Carlson (Irish and Scandinavian), Margarita Simpson (Spanish and English), Joanna Janowitz (Hebrew and Polish), Michelle Montgomery (French and English). Today there is a marked trend toward combining names of different national origins, and if it is done with good taste, names with interesting personalities can result.

Names in Harmony

When parents are considering a name for their child, they speak it aloud repeatedly in combination with their surname. They *are submitting the names to the "ear test" to determine if the series of accented and unaccented syllables produce a rhythm which is natural, pleasing and memorable.*

Our musical lyrics and poetry are based on similar patterns of rhythmic sound patterns. Among them are the trochee (an accented syllable followed by an unaccented syllable), the iamb (an unaccented syllable followed by an accented syllable), the dactyle (an accented syllable and two unaccented syllables), the anapest (two unaccented syllables followed by an accented syllable).

Any combination of these rhythmic patterns will produce a full name which is harmonious and unified: **Ronald Reagan, Katharine Hepburn,** *Elizabeth* **Taylor, Christopher Marlow, John** *Montgomery* **Page, Charlotte O'Brien, William T. Hendricks.**

To produce a name with a full sound, it is recommended that a two-syllable or three-syllable given name be used with short (one- and two-syllable) surnames: Barbara Mason, Jefferson Todd, Jacquelin Smith, Ellery Queen. A one- or two-syllable given name is suggested for long surnames: Kevin Cunningham, Joan Billingsley, Ann Rutherford, Curt Livingston.

Today's Feminine Names

This chapter is being written with the knowledge that some of its views will be considered out-of-date in the next few years, particularly in regard to the popularity of certain names. The world of names has always been subject to trends and fads, but there are some standards of good taste and good judgment which the majority of people are happy to accept.

At this time, we are enjoying a period when the traditional favorites are being joined by excellent new names in the annual lists of the Most Popular Girl's and Boy's Names and the other surveys showing the given names which parents are choosing for their children.

One point should be made clear at this time. Some parents are obsessed with the desire to give names to their children which are "different" and which will distinguish them from their peers. There is nothing wrong in such an ambition, but it should not be the primary and decisive consideration in selecting a name which will play such an important role in the child's future life. We can't emphasize too strongly that the primary responsibility of a mother and father is to give their child a name with which it will feel comfortable throughout its life, a name which will add to its own self respect, as well as the respect of its peers.

Among the names which fulfill these requirements are some of our traditional names which are as popular and well-liked in our modern culture as they have been for centuries or even thousands of years. They have a magical quality of feminine loveliness, creativity and vitality which is timeless and always new. To mention a few: Anne, Barbara, Diane, Elizabeth, Helen, Jean, Joan, Joanne, Katherine, Laura, Marian, Mary, Sarah, Susan and a dozen more that will come to your mind. You might not like one or two of these names for personal reasons, but for the majority of men and women, they have warm and welcome associations. It is quite rare that you will find a woman who has been given one of these names who is not happy with it.

In recent years, other names with outstanding appeal and character are joining them among the nation's favorites. Among them are Allison, Amy, Andrea, Annette, Beverly, Carol, Carolyn, Claire, Christine, Deborah, Deidre, Denise, Donna, Dorothy, Ellen, Faith, Frances, Heather, Jacqueline, Jennifer, Jessica, Judy, Julia, Karen, Kathleen, Kirsten, Kristen, Lisa, Liza, Lucy, Marcia, Marilyn, Maureen, Megan, Melissa, Michelle, Monica, Nancy, Nicole, Pamela, Patricia, Rachel, Rebecca, Theresa, Valerie and many, many others.

In the past few years, an exciting new group of feminine given names has been

added to the popularity lists. They are surnames which have been adopted as first names: Courtney, Darcey, Hilary, Kelly, Kimberly, Lindsay, Shelley, Sherry, Stacey, Terry, Tiffany, Tracy, Whitney. It is interesting to note the "-y" endings of these graceful names.

All of the names mentioned above are excellent considerations in choosing a name for a child, and so are hundreds of others listed in the following **Dictionary of Feminine Given Names.** If a mother wants to add a different appearance to a traditional name, she can always change the spelling slightly without making it difficult for other people to pronounce or remember.

Of course parents can create new names which are distinctive and beautiful. In such cases, it is hoped that they will keep in mind the recommendations discussed in this chapter.

Today's Masculine Names

There are boy's names which, like some girl's names, enjoy a popularity which is indestructible: Andrew, Daniel, David, James, John, Joseph, Martin, Matthew, Michael, Peter, Richard, Robert, Stephen, Thomas, William and ten or twelve others. These names have strong positive associations in the minds of both men and women. They are indisputably masculine which is the absolute requirement for a male throughout his lifetime. Surveys reveal that

these names have personalities which reflect a mixture of integrity, vitality, reliability and gentleness, as well as manliness.

They are joined in the popularity polls by some fine "new" additions (some of them are thousands of years old) which possess many of the attributes mentioned above. Among them are Adam, Alan, Anthony, Barry, Bradley, Brian, Brooks, Christopher, Clark, Corey, Craig, Curt, Darren, Dennis, Donald, Douglas, Eric, Gary, Grant, Jason, Jeffrey, Jonathan, Joshua, Keith, Kenneth, Kevin, Lawrence, Mark, Nathaniel, Nicholas, Patrick, Randall, Scott, Sean, Timothy, etc.

Parents who are searching for a "different" given name might select a surname either from the mother's or father's ancestry, or any surname which has an attractive masculine quality. It is advisable to pick a given name which will have a good nickname, always an important consideration in choosing a boy's name.

The Final Decision

We hope that some of the ideas and recommendations in this chapter will help you narrow down your list of possible choices and to make your final selection. It is also our hope that we have not made this joyous occasion seem one of undue solemnity. We know that your final decision will be the perfect one, and we congratulate you in advance.

A Dictionary of Feminine Given Names

**A**bigail (Hebrew). Father's joy.

Ada (Teutonic). Happy, prosperous.

Adele, Adela, Adeline, Adelaide (Teutonic). Noblewoman.

Adrienne, Adriane, Adriana (Latin). Black, dark. Feminine forms of Adrian.

Agatha (Greek). the virtuous one.

Agnes (Greek). The gentle, pure one.

Aileen (Greek). Light. An Irish form of Helen.

Aimee (French). The beloved one.

Alanna (Irish). My dear child.

Alberta, Albertine (Teutonic). The noble, illustrious one. Feminine forms of Albert.

Alethea (Greek). Truth.

Alexandra, Alexia, Alexis (Greek). Helper of mankind. Feminine forms of Alexander.

Alfreda (Anglo-Saxon). Elf counsellor. Elf denoted supernatural wisdom. Feminine form of Alfred.

Alice, Alicia, Alison (Teutonic). The noble, kind one.

Alma (Latin). The loving one.

Althea (Greek). One who heals and makes well.

Amanda (Latin). One worthy of love.

Amelia (Teutonic). One striving for excellence. Variant of Emily.

Amy (English). The beloved one.

Anastasia (Greek). She who will rise again; resurrection.

Andrea (Greek). The womanly one. Feminine form of Andrew.

Angela, Angelica, Angelina (Latin). The angelic one.

Ann, Anne, Anna, Annette, Anita (Hebrew). Spiritual grace.

Annabel, Annabelle, Annabella (Hebrew). Spiritual grace and beauty.

Antonia, Antoinette (Latin). The peerless one. Italian and French feminine forms of Anthony.

April (Latin). To open, as flowers open their petals.

Arabella (Latin, Teutonic). Beautiful altar; eagle heroine.

Ariadne (Greek). Very holy. From the mythological princess of Crete.

Arlene, Arleen, Arlena (Celtic). A pledge.

Astrid (Norse). Starlike.

Athanasia (Greek). The immortal one.

Audrey, Audry (Anglo-Saxon). The noble one.

Augusta, Augustine (Latin). The majestic and venerable one. Feminine form of Augustus.

Aurelia, Oriana (Latin). The golden one.

Ava (Latin). Birdlike. Also a variant of Eve, meaning "life."

**B**abette (Greek). The foreigner; the stranger. A form of Barbara.

Barbara (Greek). The foreigner; the stranger.

Beatrice, Beatrix (Latin).

One who blesses or makes happy.

Bedelia (Anglo-Saxon). *The well-dressed one.*

Belinda (Italian). *Like a wise serpent. In ancient times the serpent symbolized wisdom.*

Bella, Belle (Latin). *The beautiful one. Variants of Isabel.*

Benita (Latin). *The blessed one.*

Bernadette, Bernardine (Teutonic). *The strong one. Feminine forms of Bernard, meaning "bearlike strength."*

Bernice, Berenice (Greek). *A bringer of victory.*

Bertha (Teutonic). *The shining one.*

Beryl (Greek). *Jewel-like, precious like the beryl.*

Betty, Bessie, Betsy, Beth (Hebrew). *Consecrated to God. Forms of Elizabeth.*

Beulah (Hebrew). *One who will be married.*

Beverly (Anglo-Saxon). *From the English town of Beverly, meaning "beaver meadow."*

Bianca (Latin). *The fair, white one.*

Blanche (French). *The fair, white one.*

Bonnie, Bonny (Latin). *The charming one.*

Brenda (Celtic). *The ardent one.*

Bridget, Brigid, Brigit, Brigitta (Irish). *One with strength and wisdom.*

Brook (English). *A stream or brook.*

 **amellia, Camilla, Camille** (Latin). *A temple servant.*

Candace, Candida (Latin). *The candid and pure one.*

Cara (Celtic). *A good friend.*

Carlotta, Carla (Teutonic). *The womanly one. A feminine form of Carl or Charles.*

Carmel, Carmela (Hebrew). *God's vineyard. From Mt. Carmel in the Holy Land.*

Carmen (Latin). *Crimson; a song.*

Carol, Carole, Carola (French). *A joyous song.*

Cassandra (Greek). *Helper of mankind. A feminine form of Alexander.*

Catherine, Catharine (Greek). *The pure one.*

Cathleen (Greek). *The pure one. Irish form of Catherine.*

Cecilia, Cicely, Cecilie (Latin). *The musical one. Saint Cecilia was the patron saint of music.*

Celeste, Celesta, Celia (Latin). *Heavenly.*

Charity (Latin). *Love; charity. From caritas.*

Charlotte, Charlene (Teutonic). *The womanly one. Feminine variants of Charles.*

Charmaine (Latin). *A song or a singer.*

Cherie, Cheryl (French). *Dear one.*

Christina, Christine (Greek). *The Christian. Saint Christina was a martyred Roman noblewoman.*

Clara, Clare, Claire, Clarissa (Latin). *The bright and illustrious one.*

Clarabelle, Clarabella (Latin). *The bright and beautiful one.*

Claudia, Claudine, Claudette (Latin). *The lame one. Derived from a noble Roman family.*

Clementine (Latin). *Feminine form of Clement, meaning "merciful."*

Clotilde, Clotilda (Teutonic). *Famous maiden of battle.*

Colette (Greek). *People's victory. A contracted French form of Nicholas.*

Colleen (Celtic). *A young girl.*

Columba (Latin). *The dove.*

Constance (Latin). *The constant, steadfast one. A feminine form of Constantine, meaning "steadfast."*

Consuelo, Consuela (Spanish). *Consolation.*

Cora, Corinne (Greek). *Maiden. The name of an ancient poetess of Greece.*

Cordelia (Celtic). *Daughter of the sea.*

Cornelia (Latin). From the sacred cornel tree. Feminine of Cornelius (an ancient Roman family).

Courtney (French). From the town of Courtenai in Flanders.

Cynthia (Greek). A name for Diana, the moon-goddess, who was born on Mount Cynthus.

*aisy* (Old English). From the flower known as the "day's eyes."

Dale (Anglo-Saxon). One living in a valley.

Danielle, Daniella (Hebrew). "God is my judge." Feminine forms of Daniel.

Daphne (Greek). From the laurel tree or wreath, symbol of victory.

Darleen (Anglo-Saxon). Dearly beloved.

Dawn (Anglo-Saxon). Like daybreak.

Deanna (Latin). Bright as day or sun.

Deborah, Debora (Hebrew). From the bee, symbolizing prophecy or eloquence.

Deidre, Deirdre (Irish). The tragic one.

Delia, Della (Greek). From the island of Delos. Also a diminutive of Cordelia.

Denise, Denyse (Greek, French). St. Denys was the patron saint of France. The name was derived from St. Dionysius and from Dionysius, the Greek god of wine.

Desiree (French). The desired, beloved one.

Diana, Diane (Latin). Divine or bright as day. From the goddess of the moonlight and the hunt.

Dina, Dinah (Greek). The judged one.

Dolores, Delores (Latin, Spanish). Sorrowful. Honoring "Blessed Mary of the Sorrows."

Dominica, Dominique (Latin). Belonging to the Lord.

Dona, Donna (Latin). Lady. A title of respect.

Dora (Greek). A gift of God. A diminutive of Dorothy.

Dorcas (Greek). A gazelle. Probably a name for a baby with beautiful eyes.

Doreen (Irish). Sorrowful. A form of Dolores.

Doris (Greek). Of the ancient Dorian people of Greece.

Dorothy, Dorothea (Greek). A gift of God.

*dith, Edythe* (Anglo-Saxon). A rich gift.

Edna (Hebrew). Rejuvenation.

Edwina (Anglo-Saxon). A guardian of prosperity.

Eileen (Greek). Light. An Irish form of Helen.

Elaine (Greek). Light. A French form of Helen.

Eleanor, Eleanora, Elenore, Ellinore, Elinor (Greek). Light. Derived from Helen.

Elena (Greek). Light. A form of Helen.

Elisa, Elise, Eliza (Hebrew). Consecrated to God. Diminutives of Elizabeth.

Elizabeth, Elisabeth (Hebrew). Consecrated to God.

Ella (Anglo-Saxon). Elf-maiden. Elves were believed to possess supernatural wisdom.

Ellen, Ellyn (Greek). Light. Forms of Helen

Eloisa, Eloise (Teutonic). Famous warrior. Feminine forms of Louis.

Elsa, Elsie (Teutonic). The noble one.

Emily, Emilia, Emilie, Emmeline (Teutonic). The energetic, industrious one. Feminine forms of Emil.

Emma (Teutonic). A nurse; one who heals.

Enid (Celtic). Spotless purity.

Erica, Erika (Norse). A queenly woman. A feminine form of Eric.

Erin (Irish). Peace.

Ernestina, Ernestine (Teutonic). Serious, vigorous. Feminine forms of Ernest.

Esmeralda *(Greek). Jewel-like, precious like the emerald.*

Estelle *(Latin). Starlike.*

Esther *(Persian). Starlike.*

Ethel *(Anglo-Saxon). The noble one.*

Eugenia, Eugenie *(Greek). Well-born. A feminine form of Eugene.*

Eunice *(Greek). Happy victory.*

Eve, Eva *(Hebrew). Life.*

Evelyn *(Greek). Light. A Celtic form of Helen.*

Faith *(Latin). The faithful one. From fides.*

Fanny, Fannie *(Teutonic). Free woman. Diminutives of Frances.*

Fay, Faye *(Latin). The faithful one. Diminutives of Faith.*

Felicity, Felicia, Felice *(Latin). The happy one. From felicitas.*

Felipa, Filippa *(Greek, Latin). Lover of horses. Feminine forms of Philip.*

Fiona *(Celtic). Fair; white.*

Flora *(Latin). Flowers.*

Florence *(Latin). Flowering.*

Frances, Francesca, Francine *(Teutonic). Feminine of Francis, meaning "free."*

Freda, Frederica, Fredrika *(Teutonic). Feminine forms of Frederic meaning "peaceful ruler."*

Gabriela, Gabrielle *(Hebrew). Feminine of Gabriel, meaning "God's strength."*

Gail, Gale, Gayle *(Teutonic, Hebrew). Joyous.*

Genevieve *(Celtic). The white one.*

Georgia, Georgiana, Georgette *(Greek). Feminine variants of George, meaning "farmer."*

Geraldine *(Teutonic). Feminine of Gerald, meaning "spear ruler."*

Germaine *(Latin). A German.*

Gertrude *(Teutonic). Spear; strength.*

Gilda *(Celtic). Servant of God.*

Gladys *(Latin, Welsh). From the gladiolus flower.*

Gloria, Gloriosa *(Latin). Glorious.*

Grace, Gratia *(Latin). Divine grace. Later it came to mean charm, gracefulness, beloved.*

Greta, Gretchen *(Greek, Teutonic). Pearl. From Margaret.*

Gwendolyn, Gwendoline, Gwen *(Celtic). White brow.*

Hannah *(Hebrew). Grace. A form of Anna.*

Harriet *(Teutonic). Feminine form of Harry, meaning "home ruler."*

Hazel *(Teutonic). Light brown. Probably referring to the color of one's eyes.*

Heather *(Anglo-Saxon). From the purple-pink heather flower.*

Hedda, Hedwig *(Teutonic). Strife; fight.*

Helen, Helena, Helene *(Greek). Light. From the Greek root for "torch."*

Helga *(Norse). The holy one.*

Heloise *(Teutonic). French variant of Louis.*

Henrietta, Henriette *(Teutonic). Feminine diminutive of Henry, meaning "home ruler."*

Hermione *(Greek). High-born. From Hermes.*

Hester *(Persian). A star. Variant of Esther.*

Hilary *(Latin). Merry.*

Hilda *(Anglo-Saxon). Battle-maid.*

Hildegard *(Teutonic). A protecting battle-maid.*

Honora, Honore, Honoria *(Latin). Honor; the honored one.*

Hope *(Latin). Hope; the cherished one.*

Hortense (Latin). A gardener.

Ida *(Greek). The happy one.*

Ilone *(Hungarian). Light. A variant of Helen.*

Ilsa, Ilse *(German, Hebrew). The truthful one; the noble one. Variants of Alice.*

Imogene (Latin). Image.

Ines, Inez (Latin, Spanish). The pure one. Variants of Agnes.

Ingrid (Norse). Ingvi's daughter. Ingvi was a Norse god.

Irene, Irena (Greek). Peace.

Iris (Greek). The rainbow.

Irma (Teutonic). Noble; power.

Isabel, Isabella, Isobel (Hebrew). Consecrated to God. Variants of Elizabeth.

Isadora, Isidora (Greek). A gift from Isis, the Egyptian god.

Isolde (Celtic). The fair one.

Ita (Gaelic). Thirst.

Jacqueline *(Hebrew, French). Feminine diminutive of Jacques, meaning "the supplanter."*

Jane, Janet, Janice, Jean, Jeanne, Jeanette, Jessica, Jessie *(Hebrew). Feminine variants of John, meaning "Gracious gift of God."*

Jennifer (Celtic). The fair lady. Form of Genevieve.

Joan, Joanna, Johanna (Hebrew). Feminine variants of John, meaning "Gracious gift of God."

Jocelin, Jocelyn (Latin). Feminine diminutive of Justin, meaning "the just one."

Josephine (Hebrew). Diminutive of Joseph, meaning "Jehovah shall increase."

Joyce, Joy (Latin). Joyous, merry.

Juana, Juanita (Latin). Spanish feminine forms of John, meaning "Gracious gift of God."

Judith, Judy (Hebrew). The praiseworthy one.

Julia, Juliana, Julie, Juliette, Juliet (Latin). From the Julian family of ancient Rome. Honoring the seventh month of the calendar.

June (Latin). Youthful; one born in June.

Karen, Katherine, Kathryn, Kathleen, Katrina *(Greek). Variants of Catherine, meaning "the pure one."*

Kelly *(Celtic). A family name meaning "strife" or "contentious."*

Kimberly (English). A place name in England. Kimberly means "meadow of the shining one."

Kirsten, Kersten (Latin). Scandinavian forms of Christina, meaning "follower of Christ."

Kit, Kitty, Kate, Katie, Kathie, Kay (Greek). Diminutives of Katherine, meaning "the pure one."

Lana *(Greek). Shining.*

Laura, Laureen, Laurette *(Latin). Feminine forms of Lawrence, from laurel, the symbol of victory.*

Lea, Leah *(Hebrew). Weary.*

Lee (Anglo-Saxon). A meadowland.

Leila (Armenian). Dark beauty.

Lena (Greek). Light. Diminutive of Helena.

Lenore, Leonora, Leonore (Greek). Variants of Eleanor.

Leona, Leonie (Latin). Feminine form of Leo, meaning "the lion."

Lesley, Leslie (Celtic). A place name in Scotland. Leslie means "gray fortress."

Linda (Spanish). Beautiful.

Linette, Lynette (Celtic). From the graceful bird, the linnet.

Lisa, Lise, Lisette (Hebrew). Diminutives of Elizabeth meaning "consecrated to God."

Lois (Teutonic). *Famous warrior. Feminine form of Louis.*

Lola, Lolita (Latin). *Sorrow. From Dolores.*

Lora, Loretta (Latin). *Laurel, symbol of victory. Feminine form of Lawrence.*

Lorna (Anglo-Saxon). *The lost one.*

Lorraine (Teutonic). *From the French province of Lorraine.*

Louisa, Louise (Teutonic). *Feminine forms of Louis, meaning "famous warrior."*

Lucy, Lucille, Lucia (Latin). *Feminine forms of Lucius, meaning "light."*

Luisa, Luise (Teutonic). *Feminine forms of Louis, meaning "famous warrior."*

Lydia (Greek). *A woman from Lydia.*

**abel** (Latin). *Amiable, lovable.*

Madeleine, Madeline, Madelaine, Madelena (Hebrew). *Magnificent. Also forms of Magdalen, which means "woman of Magdala."*

Madge (Greek). *Pearl. A variant of Margaret.*

Mae, May (Latin, Hebrew). *Born in May, named for the Roman goddess Maia. Also a shortened form of Mary.*

Magdalen, Magdalene, Magda (Hebrew). *Woman of Magdala.*

Maggie, Maisie, Marge, Margie (Greek). *Pearl. Diminutives of Margaret.*

Mara (Hebrew). *Form of Mary.*

Marcia, Marsha (Latin). *From Marcus, meaning "warlike."*

Margaret (Greek). *Pearl.*

Margery, Margo, Margot (Greek). *Pearl. Variants of Margaret.*

Marguerite (Greek). *Pearl. French form of Margaret.*

Marie, Marian, Marianne, Marion, Marilyn, Maria, Mari, Marya (Hebrew). *Forms of Mary.*

Marina (Latin). *Of the sea.*

Marlene, Marleen, Marlena (Hebrew). *The uplifted one.*

Marjorie, Marjory, Margery (Greek). *Pearl. Variants of Margaret.*

Martha, Marthe (Aramaic). *Lady, mistress.*

Martina, Martine (Latin). *Feminine forms of Martin, meaning "warlike."*

Mary (Hebrew). *Meaning is obscure. Possibilities: Lady of the sea, wished-for child, bitterness, rebellion.*

Matilda, Mathilde (Teutonic). *Battle maid.*

Maud, Maude (Teutonic). *Battle maid. Variants of Matilda.*

Maura (Celtic). *The dark one.*

Maureen (Hebrew). *Irish variant of Mary.*

Mavis (Celtic). *The song thrush.*

Maxine (Latin). *Greatest. Feminine variant of Maximilian.*

Maybelle (Latin). *Amiable, lovable. Variant of Mabel.*

Mayme, Mamie (Hebrew). *Forms of Mary.*

Meghan, Megan (Greek). *The moon, the "great pearl." Possible variant of Margaret.*

Melanie (Greek). *The dark one.*

Melinda (Anglo-Saxon). *Gentle.*

Melissa (Greek). *A bee, symbolizing prophecy and eloquence.*

Melody (Latin). *The musical one.*

Mercedes (Spanish). *Mercy.*

Meredith (Celtic). *A family name meaning "sea lord."*

Michelle, Michaela (Hebrew). *"Who is like unto God." Feminine of Michael.*

Mignon (French). *Dainty.*

Mildred (Anglo-Saxon). *Gentle strength.*

Milly, Millie. *Short forms of Mildred, Camille, Emily, Millicent, etc.*

Miriam (Hebrew). *Original form of Mary.*

Moira (Gaelic). *Soft. Also a form of Mary and Maura.*

Molly (Gaelic). *Variant of Mary.*

Mona (Gaelic). *The noble one.*

Monica, Monique (Greek). The counsellor.

Morna (Gaelic). The beloved one.

Myra (Latin). The wonderful one.

Nadine, Nada (Russian). Hope.

Nancy, Nan, Nana, Nanette (Hebrew). Grace. Variants of Anna.

Naomi (Hebrew). Sweetness, pleasantness.

Natalie, Nathalie, Natasha (Latin). Birthday of Christ.

Nell, Nellie, Nelly (Greek). Light. Diminutives of Helen or Eleanor.

Nicolette, Nicola, Nikola (Greek). Feminine diminutives of Nicholas, meaning "Victory of the people."

Nina, Ninette, Ninon (Hebrew). Grace. Diminutives of Anne. Also Spanish for "little girl."

Nora, Norah, Norine, Noreen (Latin). Irish adaptations of Honora.

Norma (Latin). A model or standard.

Octavia (Latin). Feminine of Octavius, meaning "the eighth-born."

Olga (Norse). The holy one.

Olive, Olivia (Latin). The olive tree.

Olympia, Olympe (Greek). Of Olympus, heavenly.

Pamela (Greek). Gentle and loving.

Patience (Latin). The virtue of patience.

Patricia, Patrice (Latin). Feminine of Patrick, meaning "nobly-born" or "patrician."

Paula (Latin). Feminine of Paul, meaning "little."

Pauline, Paulette (Latin). Diminutives of Paula.

Pearl (Greek). Equivalent of Margaret.

Peg, Peggy (Greek). Pearl. Pet names for Margaret.

Penelope (Greek). A weaver.

Philippa (Greek). Feminine of Philip, meaning "lover of horses."

Philomena (Greek). Lover of mankind.

Phoebe (Greek). The shining or bright one.

Phyllis (Greek). A green bough.

Priscilla (Latin). Of olden times.

Prudence (Latin). The prudent one.

Rachel (Hebrew). An ewe; the gentle one.

Ramona (Teutonic). Feminine of Raymond, meaning "wise protection."

Rebecca (Hebrew). Bond of marriage. Literal meaning of Rebecca is "noose cord."

Regina, Reine (Latin). Queenly.

Reneé (Latin). Reborn. Feminine of Rene.

Rhoda (Greek). The rose.

Rhonda (Welsh). Swift river.

Ria (Spanish). A small river.

Rita (Greek). Pearl. Diminutive of Margarita.

Roberta (Teutonic). Bright fame. Feminine of Robert.

Romona (Latin). A Roman.

Rosa, Rosalie, Rosaline, Rose, Roslyn (Latin). The Rose.

Rosamond (Teutonic). Famous protection.

Rosanne (Latin). Rose of grace.

Rosemarie, Rosemary (Latin). Sea-dew; the rosemary flower.

Roxana, Roxane (Persian). Brightness.

Ruth (Hebrew). Vision of beauty.

Sacha (Greek). Russian form of Alexandra which means "helper of mankind."

Sally, Sadie (Hebrew). Princess from Sara.

Salome, Salomea (Hebrew). Peaceful.

Sandra (Greek). Diminutive form of Alexandra which means "helper of mankind."

Sara, Sarah (Hebrew). *The princess.*

Selena, Selina (Greek). *The moon.*

Sharon (Hebrew). *Wide plain.*

Sheila (Latin). *Musical. Irish form of Cecilia.*

Shelley (Anglo-Saxon). *A place name in England, meaning "wooded slope."*

Sherry (Celtic). *A young filly or foal.*

Sibyl (Greek). *Prophetess.*

Signe (Norse). *Promising victory.*

Sigrid (Norse). *Victorious counsel.*

Silvia, Sylvia (Latin). *Of the forest.*

Simona, Simone (Hebrew). *The obedient one. Feminine of Simon.*

Sonia, Sonja, Sonya (Greek). *Wisdom. A Russian variant of Sophia.*

Sophia, Sophie, Sofia (Greek). *Wisdom.*

Stella (Latin). *A star.*

Stephanie, Stefanie (Greek). *The crowned one. Feminine of Stephen.*

Susan, Susanna, Suzanne (Hebrew). *Lily.*

abitha (Aramaic). *Gazelle. Probably referring to a child's gracefulness or beautiful eyes.*

Tamara (Hebrew). *Palm tree.*

Tania, Tanya (Russian). *The moon; the great one.*

Teresa, Theresa, Therese, Terry, Terri (Greek). *The harvester.*

Thelma (Greek). *Nursling.*

Theodora, Theodosia (Greek). *Gift of God. Feminine form of Theodore.*

Theresa, Therese, Teresa, Tarese (Greek). *The harvester.*

Tiffany (English). *Manifestation of God. Form of Theophania.*

Ulrica (Teutonic). *Wolf ruler. Feminine of Ulric.*

Una (Latin). *The one.*

Ursula (Latin). *Little she-bear. St. Ursula was a famous martyr.*

alentina (Latin). *Valiant, healthy. Feminine of Valentine.*

Valerie, Valery, Valeria (Latin). *Valorous. Feminine of Valerius.*

Vanessa (Greek). *Butterfly.*

Velma (Teutonic). *Resolute protectress. Form of Wilhelmina.*

Vera (Latin). *True.*

Veronica, Veronique (Greek). *True image.*

Victoria (Latin). *The victorious one.*

Viola, Violette (Latin). *Modest, like the violet.*

Virginia (Latin). *Flowering, springlike, maidenly.*

Vivian, Vivien, Vivienne (Latin). *Lively, animated.*

anda, Wendy (German). *The wanderer.*

Wilfreda (Teutonic). *Resolute, peaceful. Feminine of Wilfred.*

Wilhelmina (Teutonic). *Resolute protectress.*

Willa, Wilma (Teutonic). *Resolute protectress. From Wilhelmina.*

Winifred (Teutonic). *Friend of peace. Possibly from the Welsh, meaning "white wave."*

Yolanda (Latin). *Modest, like the violet.*

Yvonne, Yvette (French). *The archer.*

Zoe (Greek). *Life.*

A Dictionary of Masculine Given Names

**aron** (Hebrew). Lofty mountain.

Abel (Hebrew). Breath; life.

Abraham (Hebrew). Father of the multitude.

Abram (Hebrew). High father.

Achilles (Greek). The lipless one.

Adam (Hebrew). Man created from the red earth.

Adolf, Adolph (Teutonic). Noble wolf.

Adrian (Latin). Black; dark. From the city of Adria.

Aidan (Celtic). The fiery one.

Alan, Allan, Allen, Alain (Celtic). Harmony; handsome.

Alastair (Latin). Helper of mankind. Scottish variant of Alexander.

Albert, Alberto, Albrecht (Teutonic). The noble, illustrious one.

Alexander, Alexis (Greek). Helper of mankind.

Alfred (Teutonic). Wise counselor. Literal meaning: elf counselor. The elf symbolized wisdom.

Alger (Teutonic). Noble spearman.

Aloysius, Alois (Latin). Battle glory.

Alfonso, Alphonse, Alonso, Alonzo (Teutonic). Eager for battle.

Alvin (Anglo-Saxon). Elf friend.

Ambrose (Greek). Immortal. From ambrosia, the food of the gods.

Amos (Hebrew). Burden bearer.

Anatole (Greek). Of the sunrise; of the east.

Andre, Anders, Andres, Andreas (Greek). The manly one. Forms of Andrew.

Andrew (Greek). The manly one.

Angelo (Latin). Angel. From the Latin Angelus.

Angus (Gaelic). The one choice; the exceptional one.

Anthony, Anton, Antony (Greek). The peerless one.

Archibald (Teutonic). Bold prince.

Aristides (Greek). Resolutely just.

Armand (Teutonic). Army man. French form of Herman.

Arnold (Teutonic). Eagle ruler.

Arthur (Celtic). Meaning is obscure. Possible meanings: bear; man; Thor's eagle; brave nobleman.

Athanasius (Greek). Immortal.

Aubrey (Teutonic). Elf ruler. The elf symbolized supernatural powers.

Augustus, Augustine (Latin). Majestic, venerable.

Axel (Scandinavian). Divine reward.

**aird** (Celtic). A bard or poet.

Baldwin (Teutonic). Brave friend.

Barnabas, Barnaby (Hebrew). Son of consolation.

Barry (Celtic). Excellent spearman.

Bartholomew (Hebrew). The turner of furrows, or the farmer.

Basil (Greek). Royal, kingly.

Benedict (Latin). The blessed one.

Benjamin (Hebrew). "Son of my right hand."

Bernard (Teutonic). Bearlike strength.

Berthold (Teutonic). Bright ruler.

Bertram, Bertrand (Teutonic). Bright raven.

Blaine, Blane (Celtic). Lean, yellow.

Boleslaus, Boleslaw, Boleslav (Slavic). Great glory.

Bonaventure (Latin). The lucky one.

Boniface (Latin). Doer of good.

Boris (Slavic). Fighting warrior.

Boyd (Celtic). Yellow-haired.

Bradley (Anglo-Saxon). Broad meadow.

Brendan (Irish). Firebrand; sword blade.

Brent (Anglo-Saxon). High place.

Brian (Celtic). Meaning is obscure. Regal; strong; hill.

Bruce (Scottish). From Bruys (brushwood thickets) in Normandy.

Bruno (German). Brown or dark-complected.

Byron (Old English). From the bower or cottage.

Caesar, Cesar (Latin). Meaning is obscure. Blue-eyed; long-haired.

Caleb (Hebrew). Dog. A dog symbolized loyalty and fidelity.

Calvin (Latin). The bald one.

Camillus (Latin). Temple servant.

Carl, Carlo, Carlos (Teutonic). The manly one. Variants of Charles.

Casimir (Slavic). Peaceful.

Caspar, Casper (Persian). Treasurer; horseman.

Cecil (Latin). Blind; dim-sighted.

Charles (Teutonic). The manly one.

Chester (Latin). Walled camp.

Christian (Latin). Follower of Christ.

Christopher (Greek). Bearer of Christ.

Clarence (Latin). The illustrious one.

Clark (Anglo-Saxon). A scholar or learned man.

Claud, Claude (Latin). The lame one. From a noble Roman family.

Claus (Teutonic). People's victory. Short form of Nicholas.

Clement (Latin). The merciful one.

Clive (Anglo-Saxon). A dweller by the cliffs.

Colin (Celtic). Meaning is obscure. Possibilities: young lord, young hound, dove, diminutive of Nicholas.

Conan (Celtic). The wise chief.

Conrad (Teutonic). The bold counsellor.

Constantine (Latin). The constant, firm one.

Corey (Anglo-Saxon). The chosen one.

Cormac (Irish). The charioteer.

Cornelius (Latin). Possible meanings: war horn, cornel tree. Derived from an ancient Roman family.

Cosmas, Cosmo (Greek). The world; harmony.

Craig (Celtic). A mountain crag.

Curtis, Curt (Teutonic). Courteous. Variant of Kurt.

Cuthbert (Anglo-Saxon). Famous, bright.

Cyril (Greek). The lordly one.

Cyrus (Persian). The throne; the king; the sun.

Dale (Anglo-Saxon). From the valley.

Damon, Damian (Greek). One who tames.

Dana (Teutonic). A man from Denmark.

Daniel (Hebrew). "God is my judge."

Darcy *(Old French). From the stronghold. Dark-complected (Irish).*

David *(Hebrew). Beloved; friend; commander.*

Dean *(Anglo-Saxon). From the valley.*

Demetrius *(Greek). Of Demeter, goddess of fertility and the earth.*

Denis, Dennis *(Greek). Forms of Dionysius, god of wine and the island of Nyssa.*

Derek *(Teutonic). Ruler of the people.*

Dermot, Diarmuid *(Celtic). The freeman.*

Dexter *(Latin). Right-handed; fortunate.*

Diederich, Dietrich *(Teutonic). People ruler. Forms of Theodoric.*

Diego *(Hebrew). "The supplanter." Diego is the Spanish form of James.*

Dimitri, Dmitri *(Russian). Of Demeter, goddess of fertility and the earth.*

Dirk *(Teutonic). Ruler of the people.*

Dominic *(Latin). "Belonging to the Lord."*

Donald *(Gaelic). Dark stranger; world ruler.*

Douglas *(Gaelic). One who lives near the dark water.*

Drew *(Teutonic). The skillful one, the honest one.*

Duncan *(Gaelic). The brown warrior.*

Dunstan *(Anglo-Saxon). From the dark stone.*

amon *(Celtic). Defender of property. From Edmund.*

Earl, Earle *(Teutonic). A nobleman.*

Eben *(Hebrew). The rock.*

Edgar *(Anglo-Saxon). Rich; spear. Interpreted as "defender of property."*

Edmond, Edmund *(Anglo-Saxon). Protector of property.*

Edward *(Anglo-Saxon). Guardian of property.*

Edwin *(Anglo-Saxon). Wealthy friend.*

Elias *(Hebrew). "The Lord is God." From Elijah.*

Eliot, Elliot *(Hebrew). "Jehovah is my God." From Elijah.*

Elmer *(Anglo-Saxon). Of noble fame.*

Emanuel, Emmanuel *(Hebrew). "God is with us."*

Emil, Emile *(Latin, German). Excelling; striving.*

Enoch *(Hebrew). The dedicated one.*

Eric, Erik *(Norse). Ever-ruling; kingly.*

Ernest, Ernst *(Teutonic). The serious, vigorous one.*

Ethan *(Hebrew). The strong, firm one.*

Etienne *(Greek). The crowned one. French form of Stephen.*

Eugene *(Greek). Well-born, noble.*

Eustace *(Greek). Fruitful harvest.*

Evan *(Welsh). "Gracious gift of God." Form of John.*

Everett *(Teutonic). The strong boar.*

Ezra *(Hebrew). The helper.*

abian *(Latin). A grower of beans.*

Fedor, Feodor *(Greek). "Gift of God." Slavic form of Theodore.*

Felix *(Latin). The happy one.*

Ferdinand *(Teutonic). The adventurous one.*

Fergus *(Gaelic). The best choice; the strong one.*

Florian *(Latin). Flowering.*

Floyd *(Welsh). Gray; dark complected.*

Francis, Frank, Franz *(Teutonic). Free man.*

Frederick, Frederic *(Teutonic). Peaceful ruler.*

abriel *(Hebrew). The strong one of God.*

Gary, Garry *(Teutonic). Spear ruler. Forms of Gerald.*

Gavin *(Gaelic). Battle hawk.*

Geoffrey *(Teutonic). Peace of God.*

George *(Greek). Farmer.*

Gerald *(Teutonic). Spear ruler.*

Gerard, Gerhard *(Teutonic). Strong spear.*

Gideon *(Hebrew). To strike down or to destroy.*

Gilbert *(Teutonic). Bright pledge.*

Giles *(Greek). Shield bearer.*

Giovanni *(Hebrew). "Gracious gift of God." Italian form of John.*

Girard *(Teutonic). Strong spear. Variant of Gerard.*

Giuseppe *(Hebrew). God will increase. Italian form of Joseph.*

Glen *(Gaelic). From the valley or glen.*

Godfrey *(Teutonic). God's peace.*

Godwin *(Old English). God's friend; good friend.*

Gordon *(Scottish). From the round hill.*

Graham *(Anglo-Saxon). From the gray house.*

Grant *(Latin). Great or large.*

Gregory *(Greek). The watchful one.*

Griffith *(Welsh). The fierce chieftain, the ruddy one.*

Gunter, Gunnar *(Teutonic). Bold warrior.*

Gustave, Gustavus, Gustav *(Teutonic). Goth's staff. Possible variant of Augustus.*

Guy, Guido *(Old French). Guide; lively.*

Hans *(Hebrew). "Gracious gift of God." From German Johannes (John).*

Harold *(Norse). Hardy warrior.*

Harry *(Teutonic). Home ruler. Variant of Henry.*

Harvey *(Teutonic). Hard; worthy.*

Henry *(Teutonic). Home ruler.*

Herbert *(Teutonic). Shining warrior.*

Herman *(Teutonic). Army man, soldier.*

Hilary *(Latin). Light-hearted, merry.*

Hildebrand *(Teutonic). Battle sword.*

Homer *(Greek). Pledge.*

Horace *(Latin). Of the hours.*

Howard *(Anglo-Saxon). Sword guard.*

Hubert *(Teutonic). Bright mind.*

Hugh, Hugo *(Teutonic). High intelligence.*

Humbert *(Teutonic). Home protector.*

Humphrey *(Teutonic). Peace protector.*

Hyman *(Hebrew). Life; spirit.*

Ian *(Hebrew). "Gracious gift of God." Scottish for John.*

Ignatius *(Greek). Fiery.*

Igor *(Scandinavian). Hero. Derived from god Inge.*

Ira *(Hebrew). The watchful one.*

Irvin, Irving, Irwin *(Anglo-Saxon). Friend of the sea.*

Isaac *(Hebrew). "He who laughs."*

Isaiah *(Hebrew). "Salvation of the Lord."*

Isidore *(Greek). Gift of Isis, the Egyptian goddess of the moon.*

Ivan *(Hebrew). "Gracious gift of God." Russian form of John.*

Ivor, Ivar *(Teutonic). Archer.*

Jack *(Hebrew). Nickname for John or Jacob.*

Jacob *(Hebrew). "The supplanter."*

Jacques. *French form of Jacob.*

Jaime. *Spanish form of Jacob.*

James. *English form of Jacob.*

Jan, Jon. *"Gracious gift of God." Variants of John.*

Jason *(Greek). The healer.*

Jasper *(Persian). The treasurer; the horseman. English form of Caspar.*

Jean *(Hebrew). "Gracious gift of God." French form of John.*

Jeffrey *(Teutonic). "Peace of God." Variant of Geoffrey.*

Jeremy, Jeremias (Hebrew). "Exalted of Jehovah."

Jerome (Greek). Holy name.

Jerry. Diminutive of Gerald, Gerard, Jerome, Jeremy.

Jesse (Hebrew). "Jehovah is."

Joachim (Hebrew). "The Lord will judge."

Joaquin. Spanish form of Joachim.

Joel (Hebrew). "Jehovah is God."

Johan, Johannes. Teutonic forms of John.

John (Hebrew). "Gracious gift of God."

Jonas (Hebrew). The dove.

Jonathan (Hebrew). "God has given."

Jordan (Hebrew). Flowing down.

Jose. Spanish for Joseph.

Josef. German and Austrian forms for Joseph.

Joseph (Hebrew). "God will increase."

Joshua, Josue (Hebrew). "God is salvation."

Julian, Julius (Latin). Downy bearded; youthful.

Justin, Justus (Latin). The just one; The upstanding one.

Karl (Teutonic). German and Scandinavian form of Charles, meaning "the manly one."

Karol. Slavic form of Charles.

Kasper (Persian). The treasurer; the horseman.

Keith (Celtic). The wind.

Kelly (Irish). The warrior.

Kenneth (Celtic). Handsome.

Kent (Celtic). Head chief.

Kerry (Irish). The dark one.

Kevin (Irish). Handsome.

Konrad (Teutonic). Bold.

Kurt (Teutonic). Bold counselor. German form of Konrad.

Ladislas (Slavic). Famous ruler.

Lambert (Teutonic). From the shining land.

Lance, Lancelot (Latin). One who serves; lance.

Larry, Lars. Diminutives of Lawrence.

Lawrence, Laurence (Latin). Laurel, the symbol of victory.

Lee (Anglo-Saxon). The meadow.

Leo, Leon (Latin). Lion; noble; kingly.

Leonard (Teutonic). Bold lion.

Leopold (German). The people's prince.

Leroy (Latin, French). Of the king.

Leslie (Scottish). The gray fort.

Lester (Latin). Camp of the legion.

Lewis (Teutonic). Famous warrior. English form of Louis.

Linus (Latin). Flaxen-haired.

Lionel (Latin). Young lion. From Leo.

Llewelyn, Llewellyn, Lewellen (Welsh). Lion-like; lightning.

Lloyd (Welsh). Gray, dark.

Loren, Lorenz, Lorenzo. Laurel, the symbol of victory. Forms of Laurence.

Louis (Teutonic). Famous warrior.

Lowell (Anglo-Saxon). Well-loved; little wolf.

Lucius, Lucian, Lucas (Latin). Light. Forms of Luke.

Ludwig. German form of Louis.

Louis. Spanish form of Louis.

Luke (Latin). Light.

Luther (German). Famous warrior; lute-player.

Lynn (Anglo-Saxon). Torrent; waterfall.

Malcolm (Gaelic). Follower of Columba.

Manfred (Teutonic). Man of peace.

Manuel (Hebrew). "God is with us." Variant of Emmanuel.

Mark, Marco, Marcus, Marius, Mario, Marcellus *(Latin). Warlike. From Mars, Roman god of war.*

Martin *(Latin). Warlike. From Mars, Roman god of war.*

Matthew, Matthias *(Hebrew). "The Lord's gift."*

Maurice *(Latin). Dark-complected, moorish.*

Maximilian *(Latin). Greatest.*

Maynard *(Teutonic). Strong; firm.*

Melvin, Melvyn *(Celtic). Chief; smooth forehead.*

Meredith *(Welsh). Sea chief.*

Michael *(Hebrew). "Who is like unto God?" St. Michael asked this question of Satan who compared himself to God.*

Michel, Miguel, Misha, Mikhail. *Variants of Michael.*

Miles *(Latin). Soldier.*

Milton *(Anglo-Saxon). From the mill farm or the mill town.*

Morgan *(Welsh). Sea dweller.*

Morris *(Latin). Dark-complected; Moorish.*

Mortimer *(Celtic). Sea warrior; still water.*

Morton *(Anglo-Saxon). From a home near the moor.*

Moses *(Hebrew). Saved from water.*

Murray *(Celtic). Man of the sea.*

Myles. *Variant of Miles.*

Myron *(Greek). Myrrh; fragrant.*

**apoleon** *(Greek). Lion of the city; new city.*
Nathan *(Hebrew). "A gift of God."*
Nathaniel *(Hebrew). "Gift of God."*

Neal, Neil *(Celtic). Chief, champion.*

Nicholas, Nicol *(Greek). Man of the victorious army.*

Nicol, Nicole, Nicolo, Nikolaus, Niklas, Nikolai. *Forms of Nicholas.*

Nigel *(Celtic.) Dark champion.*

Niles, Nils. *Diminutives of Nicholas.*

Noah, Noe *(Hebrew). Comfort.*

Noel *(French). Christmas.*

Norbert. *(Teutonic). Brightness.*

Norman *(Teutonic). Man from the north; man from Normandy.*

**ctavius** *(Latin). Eighth-born.*
Olaf *(Teutonic). Ancestor; peace.*
Oleg *(Russian). Holy.*
Oliver, Olivier *(Latin). Olive, symbol of peace.*

Orlando *(Teutonic). Famous in the land.*

Orson *(Latin). The bear.*

Orville *(French). Gold town.*

Oscar, Oswald *(Teutonic). Spear of Os (a pagan god); power of God.*

Osmond, Osmund *(Teutonic). Protection of Os (a pagan god); God's protection.*

Otis *(Greek). Keen of hearing.*

Otto *(Teutonic). Rich.*

Owen *(Welsh). Well-born; lamb; warrior.*

**adriac** *(Latin). Nobly born; patrician. Irish form of Patrick.*
Pascal, Pasquale *(Hebrew). One born during Passover or Easter time.*

Patrick *(Latin). Nobly born; patrician.*

Paul, Paolo, Pablo, Pavel, Pavol *(Latin). Little.*

Pedro *(Greek). The rock. Spanish for Peter.*

Percy, Percival *(French). Perceiving; piercing; a person from Perci in Normandy.*

Perry *(Anglo-Saxon). From the place where pear trees grow.*

Peter *(Greek). "The rock."*

Philip *(Greek). The horse-lover.*

Philo (Greek). Friend; lover.

Pierre, Piers, Pierce, Petrus, Pietro, Pieter. Various forms of Peter, meaning "the rock."

Quentin (Latin). From Quintus (fifth born).

**R***alph* (Teutonic). Wise counsel. Literal meaning: wolf counsel.

Ramon (Teutonic). Wise protector. Spanish form of Raymond.

Randolph, Randall (Teutonic). Guarded by wolves.

Raoul (Teutonic). Wise counsel. French form of Ralph.

Raphael, Rafael (Hebrew). God's healer.

Raymond, Redmond (Teutonic). Wise protector.

Reginald, Renaud, Rinaldo (Teutonic). Strong counsel.

Regis (Latin). Royal.

Rene (French). Reborn.

Reuben (Hebrew). "Behold, a son."

Rex (Latin). Kingly.

Ricardo. Italian form of Richard.

Richard (Teutonic). Firm ruler.

Robert (Teutonic). Bright fame.

Roberto. Italian form of Robert.

Robin (Teutonic). Bright fame. From Robert.

Roderick, Roderic (Teutonic). Noted ruler.

Roderigo. Spanish form of Roderick.

Rodney (Teutonic). Famous follower.

Roger (Teutonic). Famous spear.

Roland (Teutonic). Famed in the land.

Rollo (Teutonic). Fame; wolf. From Rudolph.

Romeo (Latin). A Roman; a pilgrim to Rome.

Ronald (Teutonic). Strong counsel. Scottish for Reginald.

Rory (Celtic). Ruddy; red-haired.

Roy (Celtic). Red; kingly.

Ruben (Hebrew). "Behold, a son."

Rudolf, Rudolph, Rudolpho (Teutonic). Famous wolf.

Rufus (Latin). Red-haired.

Rupert (Teutonic). Bright fame.

Russell (French). Ruddy; red-haired.

**S***acha* (Greek). Helper of men. Russian diminutive for Alexander.

Salvador, Salvatore (Latin). Savior.

Samson (Hebrew). Like the sun.

Samuel (Hebrew). "God hath heard."

Sancho (Spanish). Holy. From Latin sanctus.

Sandor (Greek). Helper of mankind. Hungarian for Alexander.

Santiago. Spanish for Saint James, meaning "the supplanter."

Saul (Hebrew). The longed-for one.

Scott (Celtic). A Scotsman.

Sean, Shane (Hebrew). "Gracious gift of God." Irish form of John.

Sebastian (Greek). Venerable.

Serge, Sergius, Sergei (Latin, Russian). Follower or servant.

Seth (Hebrew). The appointed one.

Seymour (Teutonic). Sea fame.

Shamus, Seamus (Hebrew). "The supplanter." Irish form of James.

Shawn (Gaelic). "Gracious gift of God." An Irish form of John.

Sheldon (Anglo-Saxon). Steep valley.

Sidney, Sydney (English). St. Denis. From St. Dionysius.

Siegfried (Teutonic). Victorious peace.

Sigmund, Sigismund (Teutonic). Victorious protection.

Silas (Latin). Of the forest.

Silvester, Sylvester (Latin). One who lived in the forest.

Simeon (Hebrew). The obedient one; one who hearkens.

Simon. Greek form of Simeon.

Sinclair (Latin). Shining, clear. From St. Clair.

Solomon (Hebrew). Peaceful.

Spencer, Spenser (Latin). A dispenser of provisions.

Stanislaus, Stanislav, Stanislaw (Slavic). Glory of the camp.

Stanley (Anglo-Saxon). Stoney field.

Stanton (Anglo-Saxon). Stone homestead.

Stephen, Stefan (Greek). The crowned one.

Stewart, Stuart (Anglo-Saxon). Manager of a household or estate.

**errence, Terry** (Latin). Smooth, tender.

Thaddeus (Hebrew). Praising God.

Theobald (Teutonic). People's prince.

Theodore (Greek). God's gift.

Theodoric (Teutonic). Ruler of the people.

Thierry. French form of Theodoric.

Thomas (Aramaic). A twin.

Thor (Teutonic). The thunder.

Tiernan, Tierney (Celtic). Kingly.

Timothy (Greek). God-fearing.

Tobias (Hebrew). "Goodness of God."

Todd (Anglo-Saxon). An old English word for "fox."

Toby. Variant of Tobias.

Tomas. (Hebrew). A twin. Spanish form of Thomas.

Tracey (Irish). War-like. Also a place name in Normandy.

Tyrone (Irish). Land of Owen.

Ulric (Teutonic). Noble ruler. Literal meaning: wolf ruler.

Urban (Latin). Of the city; town dweller.

**alentine** (Latin). Valiant, strong.

Vance (Teutonic). The thresher.

Vasily, Vassily (Slavic). Royal, kingly. A form of Basil.

Vernon (Latin). Flowering; verdant.

Victor (Latin). The victorious one.

Vincent (Latin). The conquering one.

Virgil, Vergil (Latin). Flourishing.

Vladimir (Slavic). World ruler.

**ade** (Anglo-Saxon). One who moves forward; a wanderer.

Wallace (Anglo-Saxon). Welshman; foreigner.

Walter (Teutonic). Ruler of the army.

Ward (Teutonic). A guardian.

Warner, Warren (Teutonic). A protecting friend.

Wayne (Teutonic). Wagon-maker.

Wenceslaus (Slavic). Great glory.

Wendel, Wendell (Teutonic). The wanderer.

Wesley (Anglo-Saxon). West meadow.

Wilbert, Wilbur (Teutonic). Bright of purpose or will.

Wilfred (Old English). Resolute peacemaker.

Wilhelm (Teutonic). Resolute protector.

Willard (Teutonic). Resolute, brave.

William (Teutonic). Resolute protector.

Willis (Teutonic). Son of William.

Wolfgang (Teutonic). Wolf's path.

Xavier (Basque). Bright place.

Zacharias, Zachary (Hebrew). "Remembered by God."

Our Family Memories

Autographs of Our Family,

Date	Person's Name	Relation

Relatives and Friends

Date	Person's Name	Relation

Birthdays, Anniversaries

Date	Person's Name	Relation

and Other Important Dates

Date	Person's Name	Relation

Traditional Gifts

Wedding Anniversary Gifts

The custom of celebrating wedding anniversaries with special gifts originated in very ancient times. In most cases, we do not know the origin or the exact significance of the customary gifts for the first ten anniversaries. Of course, it was quite natural that the gifts celebrating the succeeding anniversaries increased greatly.

First	Paper
Second	Cotton or Straw
Third	Leather
Fourth	Fruit, Flowers or Books
Fifth	Wooden
Sixth	Candy
Seventh	Woolen
Eighth	Pottery or Bronze
Ninth	Willow and Straw
Tenth	Tin
Twelfth	Silk and Linen
Fifteenth	Crystal
Twentieth	China
Twenty-fifth	Silver
Thirtieth	Pearl
Fortieth	Ruby or Emerald
Fiftieth	Golden
Sixtieth	Diamond
Seventieth	Diamond
Seventy-fifth	Diamond

Birthday Flowers

Each month is traditionally symbolized by flowers which are blooming in gardens during that month in temperate climates. As birthday gifts, they show special care and thoughtfulness.

January	Carnation or Snowdrop
February	Violet or Primrose
March	Daffodil or Jonquil
April	Daisy or Sweet Pea
May	Lily of the Valley or Hawthorn
June	Rose or Honeysuckle
July	Larkspur or Water Lily
August	Gladiolus or Poppy
September	Aster or Morning Glory
October	Calendula or Cosmos
November	Chrysanthemum
December	Narcissus or Holly

Birthstones

A birthstone is a precious or semi-precious gem which is a symbol of the month of a person's birth. Originally it was believed that it brought good luck.

January	**Garnet.** Constancy
February	**Amethyst.** Sincerity
March	**Bloodstone, Aquamarine.** Courage
April	**Diamond.** Innocence
May	**Emerald.** Love, Success
June	**Pearl, Moonstone.** Health
July	**Ruby, Onyx.** Contentment
August	**Sardonyx, Carnelian.** Married Happiness
September	**Sapphire.** Clear Thinking
October	**Opal, Tourmaline.** Hope
November	**Topaz.** Fidelity
December	**Turquoise.** Prosperity

Signs of the Zodiac

Astrologists draw an imaginary zone or Zodiac in the sky which follows the apparent path of the sun among the planets. The Zodiac is divided into twelve segments called Signs which are named after their constellations. Followers of astrology believe that the exact positions of the sun, moon and planets at the instant of a baby's birth influence his or her future characteristics.

 **Aries, the Ram** March 21 to April 20. Associated with Mars. Characteristics: enterprising, urgent, courageous, restless, assertive, quick-acting, passionate.

 **Taurus, the Bull** April 21 to May 21. Associated with Venus. Characteristics: steadfast, determined, practical, warm-hearted, popular, industrious.

 **Gemini, the Twins** May 22 to June 21. Associated with Mercury. Characteristics: spontaneous, versatile, imaginative, adaptable, quick-witted, mercurial.

 **Cancer, the Crab** June 22 to July 23. Associated with the Moon. Characteristics: intuitive, sensitive, loyal, sympathetic, determined, artistic, romantic.

 **Leo, the Lion** July 24 to August 23. Associated with the Sun. Characteristics: assertive, generous, proud, warm-hearted, enthusiastic, pleasure-loving.

 **Virgo, the Virgin** August 24 to September 23. Associated with Mercury. Characteristics: analytical, studious, conscientious, efficient, precise, idealistic.

 **Libra, the Scales** September 24 to October 23. Associated with Venus. Characteristics: self-expressive, charming, easy-going, compassionate, artistic.

 **Scorpio, the Scorpion** October 24 to November 22. Associated with Pluto and Mars. Characteristics: intense, purposeful, imaginative, restless, passionate.

 **Sagittarius, the Archer** November 23 to December 21. Associated with Jupiter. Characteristics: optimistic, freedom-loving, adventurous, sincere, kind, ardent.

 **Capricorn, the Goat** December 22 to January 20. Associated with Saturn. Characteristics: conscientious, ambitious, resourceful, serious, affectionate.

 **Aquarius, the Water-Carrier** January 21 to February 19. Associated with Uranus & Saturn. Characteristics: unconventional, idealistic, imaginative, daring, intuitive.

 **Pisces, the Fishes** February 20 to March 20. Associated with Neptune & Jupiter. Impressionable, compassionate, nonconforming, generous, artistic.

The Homes in Which We've Lived

When you recall the homes in which you've lived since your childhood, you will be surprised how clearly you will be able to recall the living rooms, bedrooms and kitchens, the colors, the placing of doors and windows, even the decorations, pictures and furniture.

Whether you've lived in houses or apartments, they provided the setting for your lives, and remembering them will bring back the wonderful times and all the everyday things you said and did within the walls of each of your "private worlds."

On these pages, you can record the towns and cities where you've lived, the addresses and the dates. You can describe each one in detail and even tell about its surroundings and neighborhood. You will find that reminiscing about your homes is almost like reminiscing about your lives.

Street Address _____

City _____

State _____

Country _____

Date of Purchase _____

Resided From _____ To _____

Comments Re: Surroundings,
Neighborhood, Reason for Moving _____

_____

_____

_____

_____

_____

_____

_____

_____

_____

_____

_____

_____

Street Address _____

City _____

State _____

Country _____

Date of Purchase _____

Resided From _____ To _____

Comments Re: Surroundings,
Neighborhood, Reason for Moving _____

_____

_____

_____

_____

_____

_____

_____

_____

_____

_____

_____

_____

Street Address _____

City _____

State _____

Country _____

Date of Purchase _____

Resided From _____ *To* _____

Comments Re: Surroundings,
Neighborhood, Reason for Moving _____

_____

_____

_____

_____

_____

_____

_____

_____

_____

_____

_____

_____

_____

_____

_____

_____

_____

_____

_____

Street Address _____

City _____

State _____

Country _____

Date of Purchase _____

Resided From _____ *To* _____

Comments Re: Surroundings,
Neighborhood, Reason for Moving _____

_____

_____

_____

_____

_____

_____

_____

_____

Date _____

Place Photo Here

Place Photo Here

Street Address _____
City _____
State _____
Country _____
Date of Purchase _____
Resided From _____ To _____
Comments Re: Surroundings,
Neighborhood, Reason for Moving _____

_____
_____
_____
_____
_____
_____
_____
_____
_____
_____
_____
_____
_____
_____
_____
_____
_____
_____
_____

Date _____

Street Address _____
City _____
State _____
Country _____
Date of Purchase _____
Resided From _____ To _____
Comments Re: Surroundings,
Neighborhood, Reason for Moving _____

_____
_____
_____
_____
_____
_____
_____
_____
_____

Our Family Weddings

Weddings are the joyous and well-remembered events in every family when relatives and friends come from near and far to witness the solemn ceremonies and to participate in the happy festivities. Each wedding is a time of deep religious significance, of joyous celebration and of warm reunion with the people who are important to us.

On these pages, you will have the opportunity to record your family's past and future weddings: the dates, places, names of the clergymen or officials performing the ceremonies, the best men, maids of honor, ushers, bridesmaids, relatives, friends and guests.

You will also be able to describe the ceremonies, receptions, prenuptial parties, honeymoon travels and any other events which you want to be remembered.

Husband's
Name _____

Birth Date _____

Wife's
Maiden Name _____

Birth Date _____

Date of Ceremony _____

Place of Ceremony _____

City _____

State _____

Married By _____

Best Man _____

Maid of
Honor _____

Comments _____

_____

_____

_____

Husband's
Name _____

Birth Date _____

Wife's
Maiden Name _____

Birth Date _____

Date of Ceremony _____

Place of Ceremony _____

City _____

State _____

Married By _____

Best Man _____

Maid of
Honor _____

Comments _____

_____

_____

_____

Husband's
Name _____

Birth Date _____

Wife's
Maiden Name _____

Birth Date _____

Date of Ceremony _____

Place of Ceremony _____
_____

City _____

State _____

Married By _____
_____

Best Man _____
_____

Maid of
Honor _____
_____

Comments _____
_____
_____
_____
_____
_____
_____
_____
_____
_____
_____
_____
_____
_____
_____

Husband's
Name _____

Birth Date _____

Wife's
Maiden Name _____

Birth Date _____

Date of Ceremony _____

Place of Ceremony _____
_____

City _____

State _____

Married By _____
_____

Best Man _____
_____

Maid of
Honor _____
_____

Comments _____
_____
_____
_____
_____
_____
_____
_____
_____
_____
_____
_____
_____
_____
_____

Husband's
Name _____

Birth Date _____

Wife's
Maiden Name _____

Birth Date _____

Date of Ceremony _____

Place of Ceremony _____

City _____

State _____

Married By _____

Best Man _____

Maid of
Honor _____

Comments _____

_____

_____

_____

_____

_____

_____

_____

_____

_____

_____

_____

_____

_____

_____

Husband's
Name _____

Birth Date _____

Wife's
Maiden Name _____

Birth Date _____

Date of Ceremony _____

Place of Ceremony _____

City _____

State _____

Married By _____

Best Man _____

Maid of
Honor _____

Comments _____

_____

_____

_____

_____

_____

_____

_____

_____

_____

_____

_____

_____

_____

_____

The Schools We've Attended

On these pages, you can outline the educational background of each member of your family. We suggest that you start with yourselves and list your schools and the dates when you attended them: the elementary and high schools, trade schools, colleges, universitites, post graduate courses, night schools and home study courses. Tell about your scholastic achievements, favorite subjects, memorable experiences, extra-curricular activities, clubs, sports, special teachers and friends, even your escapades. Then, follow the same procedure with your parents, children and other members of your family.

Name _____

School _____

Dates _____

City _____

State _____

Comments _____

_____

_____

_____

_____

_____

_____

_____

_____

_____

_____

_____

_____

_____

_____

_____

_____

_____

Name _____

School _____

Dates _____

City _____

State _____

Comments _____

_____

_____

_____

_____

_____

_____

_____

_____

_____

_____

_____

_____

_____

_____

_____

_____

_____

Name

School

Dates

City

State

Comments

Name

School

Dates

City

State

Comments

Name

School

Dates

City

State

Comments

Name

School

Dates

City

State

Comments

Name _____

School _____

Dates _____

City _____

State _____

Comments _____

_____

_____

_____

_____

_____

_____

_____

_____

_____

_____

_____

Name _____

School _____

Dates _____

City _____

State _____

Comments _____

_____

_____

_____

_____

_____

_____

_____

_____

_____

_____

_____

Name _____

School _____

Dates _____

City _____

State _____

Comments _____

_____

_____

_____

_____

_____

_____

_____

_____

_____

_____

_____

Name _____

School _____

Dates _____

City _____

State _____

Comments _____

_____

_____

_____

_____

_____

_____

_____

_____

_____

_____

_____

Name

School

Dates

City

State

Comments

Name

School

Dates

City

State

Comments

Name

School

Dates

City

State

Comments

Name

School

Dates

City

State

Comments

Our Best Friends

Just remembering your friends and writing about them will be a very heartwarming experience for you and all the members of your family. A good friend is like a brother or sister in many ways—someone in whom you can confide and share your thoughts and experiences, so any history of your family would be incomplete without them. When you record the dates and places of your friendships of the past and present, also describe your memorable experiences with these people of all ages and tell why they are so important to you.

Name _____

Date _____

City _____

State _____

Name _____

Date _____

City _____

State _____

Name

Date

City

State

Name

Date

City

State

Name

Date

City

State

Name

Date

City

State

Name ——————————————
Date ——————————————
City ——————————————
State ——————————————

——————————————
——————————————
——————————————
——————————————
——————————————
——————————————
——————————————
——————————————
——————————————
——————————————

Name ——————————————
Date ——————————————
City ——————————————
State ——————————————

——————————————
——————————————
——————————————
——————————————
——————————————
——————————————
——————————————
——————————————
——————————————
——————————————

Name ——————————————
Date ——————————————
City ——————————————
State ——————————————

——————————————
——————————————
——————————————
——————————————
——————————————
——————————————
——————————————
——————————————
——————————————
——————————————

Name ——————————————
Date ——————————————
City ——————————————
State ——————————————

——————————————
——————————————
——————————————
——————————————
——————————————
——————————————
——————————————
——————————————
——————————————
——————————————

Our Professions, Occupations, Trades and Crafts

When you begin listing the many endeavors and callings in which your family has been engaged, you will be amazed at their scope and variety. We suggest that you start with your own "employment record" by writing about the first jobs of your childhood and continue to the present, including dates, names of firms, positions, promotions, salaries, successes, failures, memorable experiences, fellow workers, associates, etc. Repeat this procedure for other members of your family.

Also give an account of the businesses started by your relatives and of the achievements of men and women who were engaged in the arts, entertainments, politics and sports. Whenever possible you might also add employment registration numbers (for instance, social security numbers) for future reference.

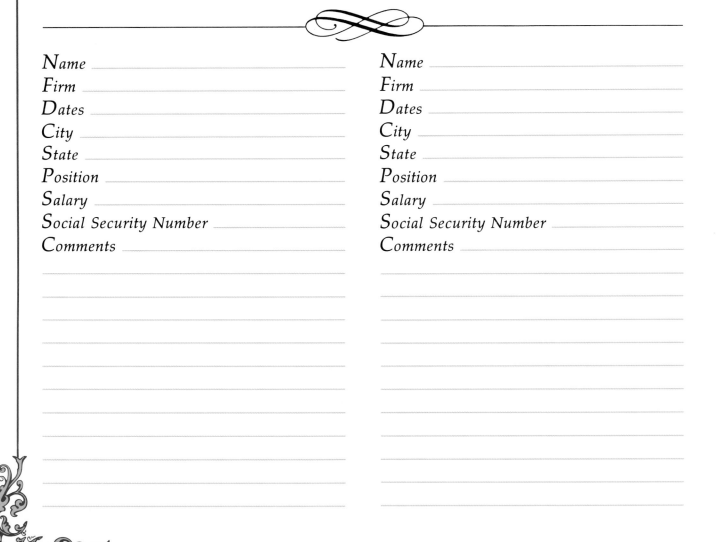

Name _____

Firm _____

Dates _____

City _____

State _____

Position _____

Salary _____

Social Security Number _____

Comments _____

Name _____

Firm _____

Dates _____

City _____

State _____

Position _____

Salary _____

Social Security Number _____

Comments _____

Name

Firm

Dates

City

State

Position

Salary

Social Security Number

Comments

Name

Firm

Dates

City

State

Position

Salary

Social Security Number

Comments

Name

Firm

Dates

City

State

Position

Salary

Social Security Number

Comments

Name

Firm

Dates

City

State

Position

Salary

Social Security Number

Comments

Name _____
Firm _____
Dates _____
City _____
State _____
Position _____
Salary _____
Social Security Number _____
Comments _____

_____
_____
_____
_____
_____
_____
_____
_____
_____

Name _____
Firm _____
Dates _____
City _____
State _____
Position _____
Salary _____
Social Security Number _____
Comments _____

_____
_____
_____
_____
_____
_____

Name _____
Firm _____
Dates _____
City _____
State _____
Position _____
Salary _____
Social Security Number _____
Comments _____

_____
_____
_____
_____
_____
_____
_____
_____
_____

Name _____
Firm _____
Dates _____
City _____
State _____
Position _____
Salary _____
Social Security Number _____
Comments _____

_____
_____
_____
_____
_____
_____

Name

Firm

Dates

City

State

Position

Salary

Social Security Number

Comments

Name

Firm

Dates

City

State

Position

Salary

Social Security Number

Comments

Name

Firm

Dates

City

State

Position

Salary

Social Security Number

Comments

Name

Firm

Dates

City

State

Position

Salary

Social Security Number

Comments

Our Talents, Skills and Hobbies

The subjects you write about on these pages can embrace the entire range of your family's interests and talents. For instance, sketching, chess, painting, sculpture, drama, music, theatre, miniature making, sewing, needlework, knitting, macrame, gardening, dancing, cooking, ceramics, photography, model making, carpentry, woodcarving, amateur radio, tropical fish raising, weaving, crossword puzzles, etc.

When you add "collecting" hobbies to this list, the possibilities become almost infinite: baseball cards, stamps, nostalgia items, beads, butterflies, buttons, dolls and autographs to mention a few of the hundreds of categories.

Name _____
Dates _____
Subject _____
Hobbies _____

Approximate Value _____
Comments _____

Name _____
Dates _____
Subject _____
Hobbies _____

Approximate Value _____
Comments _____

Name _____
Dates _____
Subject _____
Hobbies _____

Approximate Value _____
Comments _____

Name _____
Dates _____
Subject _____
Hobbies _____

Approximate Value _____
Comments _____

Name

Dates

Subject

Hobbies

Approximate Value

Comments

Name

Dates

Subject

Hobbies

Approximate Value

Comments

The Clubs and Organizations We've Joined

In our country, there are an amazing number of organizations which can be joined by people sharing common interests. There are clubs for every type of school activity, sororities, fraternities, PTAs, civic committees, charity and welfare groups, trade and labor unions, fraternal societies, professional and business associations, veterans organizations, sports and hobby clubs, social and bridge clubs, alumni associations, church societies, formal and informal organizations of every description. When you start listing them here, you will be surprised at the number which the members of your family have joined.

Name _____

Dates _____

Organization _____

Comments _____

_____

_____

_____

Name _____

Dates _____

Organization _____

Comments _____

_____

_____

_____

Name
Dates
Organization
Comments

Name
Dates
Organization
Comments

Our Family's History of Military Service

Here you can compile a record of the military lives of the members of your family and of your ancestors in this country and in their native land. When possible, show their branch of service, ranks and grades, promotions, duty stations, citations and decorations, battles and engagements. Most interesting of all will be their stories about their friends, travels, adventures, misadventures and their personal impressions of military life.

If you wish to obtain the military service records of a member of your family, alive or deceased, see page 19.

Name _____

Dates _____

Branch of Service _____

Service Number _____

Rank/Grade _____

Citations/Decorations _____
_____

Battles/Engagements _____
_____

Duty Stations & Dates _____
_____

Location of Military Service Papers ___

Comments _____
_____
_____
_____
_____

_____

Name _____ Date ___

Place Photo Here

264

Name _____

Dates _____

Branch of Service _____

Service Number _____

Rank/Grade _____

Citations/Decorations _____

Battles/Engagements _____

Duty Stations & Dates _____

Location of Military Service Papers _____

Comments _____

_____

_____

_____

_____

_____

_____

_____

_____

_____

_____

_____

_____

_____

_____

_____

Place Photo Here

Name _____ Date _____

Name

Dates

Branch of Service

Service Number

Rank/Grade

Citations/Decorations

Battles/Engagements

Duty Stations & Dates

Location of Military Service Papers

Comments

Place Photo Here

Name   Date

Name _____

Dates _____

Branch of Service _____

Service Number _____

Rank/Grade _____

Citations/Decorations _____

_____

Battles/Engagements _____

_____

Duty Stations & Dates _____

_____

_____

Location of Military Service Papers _____

_____

Comments _____

_____

_____

Name _____ *Date* _____

Name _____

Dates _____

Branch of Service _____

Service Number _____

Rank/Grade _____

Citations/Decorations _____

_____

Battles/Engagements _____

_____

Duty Stations & Dates _____

_____

_____

Location of Military Service Papers _____

_____

Comments _____

_____

_____

_____

_____

_____

_____

_____

_____

_____

_____

_____

_____

_____

_____

_____

_____

_____

_____

_____

Place Photo Here

Name _____

Dates _____

Branch of Service _____

Service Number _____

Rank/Grade _____

Citations/Decorations _____

_____

Battles/Engagements _____

_____

Duty Stations & Dates _____

Location of Military Service Papers _____

_____

Comments _____

_____

_____

_____

_____

_____

_____

_____

_____

_____

_____

_____

_____

_____

_____

_____

Place Photo Here

Name _____ Date _____

Name

Dates

Branch of Service

Service Number

Rank/Grade

Citations/Decorations

Battles/Engagements

Duty Stations & Dates

Location of Military Service Papers

Comments

Name _____ *Date* _____

Place Photo Here

Family Gatherings and Reunions

Many family gatherings are holiday celebrations which are traditionally held year after year at the homes of the same members of the family. Others are special parties when we assemble for birthdays, anniversaries or for other special occasions. They are always happy opportunities to see our loved ones again, to renew cherished relationships and to relive our family traditions.

Future family gatherings and reunions will also offer you wonderful opportunities to tell them about this book, to arrange interviews, and to gather further information about your family history.

On these pages, you can describe these festive get-togethers and list all the friends and relatives who attended them.

Occasion _____

Date _____

Friends/Relatives Who Attended _____

_____

_____

_____

_____

_____

_____

_____

_____

_____

_____

_____

_____

_____

_____

_____

_____

_____

_____

_____

Occasion _____

Date _____

Friends/Relatives Who Attended _____

_____

_____

_____

_____

_____

_____

_____

_____

_____

_____

_____

_____

_____

_____

_____

_____

_____

_____

_____

Occasion _____

Date _____

Friends/Relatives Who Attended _____

_____

_____

_____

_____

_____

_____

_____

_____

_____

_____

_____

_____

_____

_____

_____

_____

_____

_____

_____

_____

_____

_____

_____

_____

_____

_____

_____

_____

Occasion _____

Date _____

Friends/Relatives Who Attended _____

_____

_____

_____

_____

_____

_____

_____

_____

_____

_____

_____

_____

_____

_____

_____

_____

_____

_____

_____

_____

_____

_____

_____

_____

_____

_____

_____

_____

*O*ccasion _____

*D*ate _____

*F*riends/Relatives Who Attended _____

_____

_____

_____

_____

_____

_____

_____

_____

_____

_____

_____

_____

_____

_____

_____

_____

_____

_____

_____

_____

_____

_____

_____

_____

*O*ccasion _____

*D*ate _____

*F*riends/Relatives who attended _____

_____

_____

_____

_____

_____

_____

_____

_____

_____

_____

_____

_____

_____

_____

_____

_____

_____

_____

_____

_____

_____

_____

_____

_____

Occasion _____

Date _____

Friends/Relatives Who Attended

_____

_____

_____

_____

_____

_____

_____

_____

_____

_____

_____

_____

_____

_____

_____

_____

_____

_____

_____

_____

_____

_____

_____

_____

_____

Occasion _____

Date _____

Friends/Relatives Who Attended

_____

_____

_____

_____

_____

_____

_____

_____

_____

_____

_____

_____

_____

_____

_____

_____

_____

_____

_____

_____

_____

_____

_____

_____

_____

*O*ccasion _____

*D*ate _____

*F*riends/Relatives Who Attended _____

_____
_____
_____
_____
_____
_____
_____
_____
_____
_____
_____
_____
_____
_____
_____
_____
_____
_____
_____
_____
_____
_____
_____
_____
_____
_____
_____

*O*ccasion _____

*D*ate _____

*F*riends/Relatives Who Attended _____

_____
_____
_____
_____
_____
_____
_____
_____
_____
_____
_____
_____
_____
_____
_____
_____
_____
_____
_____
_____
_____
_____
_____
_____
_____
_____
_____

Our Family's Cherished Traditions

Every family has its own beloved traditions. Some are so old that we often don't know how or when they began, while others have been born within our own lifetime. Whether old or new, we hope that our children will pass them on to their children because these cherished traditions give to each family its own special character and individuality.

Holidays and reunions are the happy times when families are united in their traditions. The old songs are sung, and the remembered poems are recited. All the old favorite stories are retold, and the witty and wise quotations of our parents and grandparents are repeated.

And, of course, there are many traditional sayings and ways of doing things which we have inherited and which are a part of our everyday lives.

Event _____
Date _____

_____
_____
_____
_____
_____
_____
_____
_____
_____
_____
_____
_____
_____
_____
_____
_____
_____
_____
_____
_____
_____

Event _____
Date _____

_____
_____
_____
_____
_____
_____
_____
_____
_____
_____
_____
_____
_____
_____
_____
_____
_____
_____
_____
_____
_____

Event _____
Date _____

Event _____
Date _____

Event

Date

Event

Date

*E*vent
*D*ate

*E*vent
*D*ate

Memorable Personalities in Our Lives

Certain unusual people have probably played vital and unforgettable roles in your lives as individuals and as a family. They might be teachers who encouraged your interests or your choice of career, clergymen who influenced you spiritually, fellow workers or superiors who took an interest in your success, thinkers and writers whose ideas inspired you, friends and relatives who supported you when you needed them the most. In short, they are the men and women whose words, ideas or action have left a deep and enduring impression upon you.

You might be on close personal terms with these memorable individuals, or you might never have met them face to face, but their effect upon you and your family has been a lasting one.

Personality _____

_____

_____

_____

_____

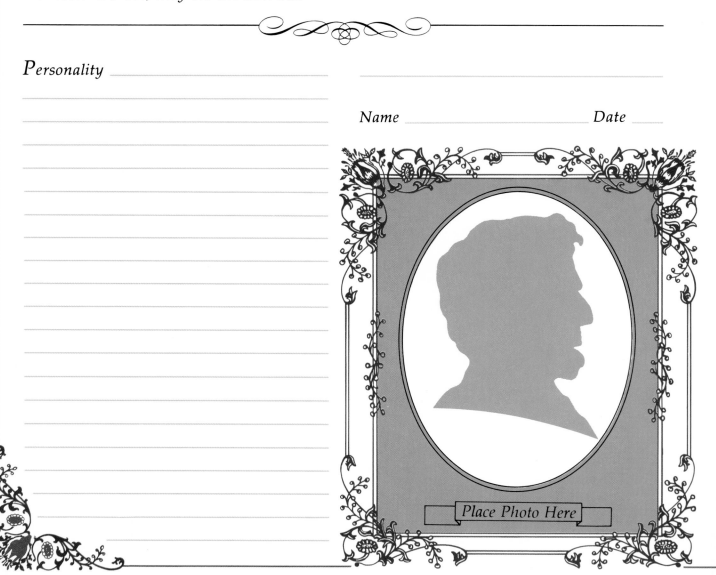

Name _____ Date _____

Place Photo Here

Place Photo Here

Personality

Name   Date   Name   Date

Personality

Place Photo Here

281

Place Photo Here

Name _____ Date _____

Name _____ Date _____

Place Photo Here

Place Photo Here

Name _____ Date _____

Great Moments in Our Family History

You can describe on these pages the outstanding events, achievements and adventures which were witnessed or experienced by the living members of your family or by your ancestors. The list of these thrilling and unique occasions might include receiving a highly-prized honor, meeting a famous person, witnessing an historic event, winning military distinction, scoring the winning touchdown, getting the lead in a play, catching the fish of a lifetime. Any event which you consider thrilling and meaningful should be recorded here.

Event _____

Date _____

_____
_____
_____
_____
_____
_____
_____
_____
_____
_____
_____
_____
_____
_____
_____
_____
_____
_____
_____

Event _____

Date _____

_____
_____
_____
_____
_____
_____
_____
_____
_____
_____
_____
_____
_____
_____
_____
_____
_____
_____
_____

Event

Date

Event

Date

Event

Date

Event

Date

Event

Date

Event

Date

The Elections We Remember

When you look back over the lives of the men and women in your family, you will be surprised to find how many of you were involved either as candidates for office or as ardent supporters. In the school years there were elections for clubs, teams, groups, sororities, fraternities, etc. In later life, there are social clubs, business and professional organizations, unions, charity groups, fraternal and veteran groups, PTAs and many other types of organizations.

Of course, there were also elections for local, state and national political offices. You or your relatives or friends might have been candidates, active supporters or just concerned citizens who were deeply affected in the outcome of a political campaign. On these pages, you can write about the elections whose outcomes were important to the members of your family.

Name _____
Election _____
Date _____
Outcome _____
Comments _____
_____
_____
_____

Name _____
Election _____
Date _____
Outcome _____
Comments _____
_____
_____
_____

Name _____
Election _____
Date _____
Outcome _____
Comments _____
_____
_____
_____

Name _____
Election _____
Date _____
Outcome _____
Comments _____
_____
_____
_____

Name _____
Election _____
Date _____
Outcome _____
Comments _____
_____
_____
_____
_____
_____

Name _____
Election _____
Date _____
Outcome _____
Comments _____
_____
_____
_____
_____
_____

Name _____
Election _____
Date _____
Outcome _____
Comments: _____
_____
_____
_____
_____
_____

Name _____
Election _____
Date _____
Outcome _____
Comments _____
_____
_____
_____
_____
_____

Name _____
Election _____
Date _____
Outcome _____
Comments _____
_____
_____
_____
_____
_____

Name _____
Election _____
Date _____
Outcome _____
Comments _____
_____
_____
_____
_____
_____

Crises
We've Overcome

In the history of your family, your ancestors were able to survive war, invasion, famine and oppression through their courage and determination.

Today's families must also face its crises. We've been confronted by serious fires, hurricanes, floods, blizzards and tragic accidents. We've suffered through wars and depressions, and many of us have survived financial reversals and serious personal problems.

Here you can describe the crises encountered by your family and tell how you were able to overcome them.

Dates _____

Dates _____

Dates

Date

*D*ates _____

*D*ates _____

Dates _____

Dates _____

Our Aspirations

Most teen-age girls have dreams of becoming a glamorous film star, an exciting poetess or a dedicated nurse. Teen-age boys nurse secret ambitions of being a big-league ballplayer, a daring astronaut or a great scientist. On these pages, you can recall your early aspirations and how they changed through the years to become your present hopes for the future. And you can record the ambitions of your children as they, too, are influenced by the passing of time.

Name _____

Date _____

Name _____

Date _____

Name

Date

Name

Date

Name

Date

Name

Date

Memorable Vacations and Travels

For most of us, vacation times are among the highlights of our lives. The members of your family will probably be able to recall every vacation which you have enjoyed together. Whether you spent only a few days or several weeks, whether you went to the seashore, the ski slopes, the woods or on a long automobile trip, just talking about them will bring back a flood of memories.

When, where and with whom did you go? Where did you stay and whom did you meet? What were the unusual things that happened and what did you enjoy the most? In describing your vacations here, you and your family will relive those happy times and write a precious record for future years.

When, where and with whom did you go?

_____
_____
_____

Where did you stay and with whom did you meet?

Place _____
Date _____

What were the most unusual things that happened and what did you enjoy the most? _____
_____
_____

Other comments:
_____
_____
_____
_____
_____
_____

When, where and with whom did you go?

_____
_____
_____

Where did you stay and with whom did you meet?

Place _____
Date _____

What were the most unusual things that happened and what did you enjoy the most? _____
_____
_____

Other comments:
_____
_____
_____
_____
_____
_____

Our Favorite Sports

All the athletic enthusiasts in your family can join in writing this chapter. Each of them can tell about the exhilarating recreations they most enjoy: swimming, jogging, tennis, golf, skiing, hiking, fishing, hunting, bowling, racquetball, volleyball, surfing, snowmobiling, motorcycling, etc.

You'll also want to describe the participation and achievements of the younger members of the family in team sports like basketball, football, baseball, gymnastics, soccer and cheerleading. And don't forget your own athletic experiences in your undergraduate days.

Name	Sport	Position

Name	Sport	Position

The Athletes We've Admired

When you and your family discuss your favorite athletes, you'll probably find that you admire them for their personalities and characters as well as their athletic achievements.

Perhaps some of them were your classmates or people whom you know personally. Of course, many will be the all-time sports stars like baseball's Pete Rose and Joe DiMaggio, golfers Ben Hogan and Jack Nicklaus, tennis champion Chris Evert and Bjorn Borg, track stars Babe Didriksen and Jesse Owens, Olympic heroes Eric Heiden and Mark Spitz, football's Johnny Unitas and O. J. Simpson, basketball's Bill Russell and Larry Byrd.

You might also list your favorite teams like the American hockey players who won the 1980 Olympics, or a World's Series championship team, or your Pony League team.

Athlete	Sport	Event

Athlete	Sport	Event

The Automobiles We Remember

Our automobiles seem to be the mechanical members of our family. They take us almost everywhere we go, to school and to work, to the doctor and dentist, to the theatre and the ball game, to church and to the store. They accompany us on our vacations and travels.

There's no living without them, so we suggest that you dedicate these pages to the automobiles in your lives. You might begin by describing your first car, and then write about the others—their makes, models, years, colors, lengths of service as well as their idiosyncracies, personalities and adventures.

Make _____ Model _____

Year _____ Color _____

License Plate # _____

Length of Service _____

Comments _____

_____

_____

Make _____ Model _____

Year _____ Color _____

License Plate # _____

Length of Service _____

Comments _____

_____

_____

Make _____ Model _____
Year _____ Color _____
License Plate # _____
Length of Service _____
Comments _____
_____
_____
_____
_____
_____
_____
_____
_____
_____
_____

Make _____ Model _____
Year _____ Color _____
License Plate # _____
Length of Service _____
Comments _____
_____
_____
_____
_____
_____
_____
_____
_____
_____
_____

Make _____ Model _____
Year _____ Color _____
License Plate # _____
Length of Service _____
Comments _____
_____
_____
_____
_____
_____
_____
_____
_____
_____
_____

Make _____ Model _____
Year _____ Color _____
License Plate # _____
Length of Service _____
Comments _____
_____
_____
_____
_____
_____
_____
_____
_____
_____
_____

Our Prized
Family Possessions

Some of the possessions which you value most highly have probably been passed on to you generation after generation, and they are as much a part of your family history as the names, dates and events which you have recorded in this book. Whether they are articles of art, furniture, jewelry, books or personal keepsakes, they serve as reminders of the wonderful people of the past.

We urge you to list them here, describing them in detail and noting their original owners so that future members of your family will appreciate their true worth. And don't forget to inventory the precious articles which you have acquired and the collections which you have started for they will become the treasured heirlooms of the future.

Item _____

Original Owner _____

Age _____ Valued At _____

Date _____

Date _____

Place Photo Here

Place Photo Here

Item

Original Owner

Age _____ *Valued At*

Date

Date

Item

Original Owner

Age _____ *Valued At*

Date

Date

Place Photo Here

Place Photo Here

Place Photo Here

Date _____

Item _____
Original Owner _____
Age _____ Valued At _____
Date _____

_____
_____
_____
_____
_____
_____
_____
_____
_____
_____
_____

Date _____

Item _____
Original Owner _____
Age _____ Valued At _____
Date _____

_____
_____
_____
_____
_____
_____
_____
_____
_____
_____
_____

Item _____

Original Owner _____

Age _____ Valued At _____

Date _____

_____

_____

_____

_____

_____

_____

_____

_____

_____

Date _____

Item _____

Original Owner _____

Age _____ Valued At _____

Date _____

_____

_____

_____

_____

_____

_____

_____

_____

_____

Date _____

Place Photo Here

Place Photo Here

Place Photo Here

Place Photo Here

Date _____

Item _____
Original Owner _____
Age _____ Valued At _____
Date _____

Date _____

Item _____
Original Owner _____
Age _____ Valued At _____
Date _____

Item _____

Original Owner _____

Age _____ *Valued At* _____

Date _____

_____

_____

_____

_____

_____

_____

_____

_____

_____

Date _____

Item _____

Original Owner _____

Age _____ *Valued At* _____

Date _____

_____

_____

_____

_____

_____

_____

_____

_____

_____

Date _____

Place Photo Here

Place Photo Here

Our Favorite Books and Poems

Just think of the many books which have made a lasting and vivid impression on your memory: the picture books and fairy tales of your childhood, your first school books in elementary school, the literary works and weighty textbooks of high school and college. Then there are the books which you've read in later years for entertainment and relaxation or to further your intellectual and spiritual life.

Of all the books and poems you've read, ten or fifteen will stand out in your mind, either for the pure enjoyment which they brought you, or for the contribution which they made to your thinking or fund of knowledge. Here you can list your family's favorites and tell why they were selected to be remembered in these pages.

Title	Author	Comments

Title	Author	Comments

Fur, Fins, and Feathers — The Pets in Our Lives

For a child growing up (and for most grown-ups), a pet is a very special friend— a member of the family. Pets come in a variety of sizes and shapes, colors and breeds. They come with and without pedigrees, and their personalities are as different as the human members of a family. Whether a dog, cat, bird, fish, turtle, rabbit, horse, monkey or some other exotic pet, they become parts of our everyday lives. On these pages you can describe each of them: their appearance, temperament, habits, tricks and idiosyncrasies.

Name _____

Breed _____ Date _____

Appearance _____

Temperament _____

Habits _____

Tricks _____

Idiosyncrasies _____

Comments _____

_____

_____

_____

_____

_____

_____

_____

_____

_____

Name _____

Breed _____ Date _____

Appearance _____

Temperament _____

Habits _____

Tricks _____

Idiosyncrasies _____

Comments _____

_____

_____

_____

_____

_____

_____

_____

_____

_____

Name _____

Breed _____ Date _____

Appearance _____

Temperament _____

Habits _____

Tricks _____

Idiosyncrasies _____

Comments _____

_____

_____

_____

_____

_____

_____

_____

_____

_____

Place Photo Here

Name _____ Date _____   Name _____ Date _____

Name _____

Breed _____ Date _____

Appearance _____

Temperament _____

Habits _____

Tricks _____

Idiosyncrasies _____

Comments _____

_____

_____

_____

_____

_____

_____

Place Photo Here

Place Photo Here

Place Photo Here

Name _____ Date _____

Name _____ Date _____

Name _____
Breed _____ Date _____
Appearance _____
Temperament _____
Habits _____
Tricks _____
Idiosyncrasies _____

Name _____
Breed _____ Date _____
Appearance _____
Temperament _____
Habits _____
Tricks _____
Idiosyncrasies _____

Comments _____

Comments _____

Name _____

Breed _____ *Date* _____

Appearance _____

Temperament _____

Habits _____

Tricks _____

Idiosyncrasies _____

_____

Comments _____

_____

_____

_____

_____

Name _____

Breed _____ *Date* _____

Appearance _____

Temperament _____

Habits _____

Tricks _____

Idiosyncrasies _____

_____

Comments _____

_____

_____

_____

_____

Name _____ *Date* _____

Name _____ *Date* _____

Place Photo Here

Place Photo Here

The Songs and Dances We Remember

Songs and music are truly magic ingredients of our lives which bring back the happy memories of our childhood and youth, our school days and courtship, our marriage and maturity. We relive the joyous and meaningful times of the past when we hear just a few bars of a melody or words of a lyric. When writing these pages, be sure to have the other members of the family participate by suggesting the songs which are most significant to them.

Dances which you've learned also evoke memories of happy times. Remember the innocent dances in kindergarten? And the basic box or two-step, waltz, fox-trot, swing, polka, rhumba, tango, jitterbug, square dance, twist, rock and roll, disco and others?

Name	Songs/Dances	Year

Name	Songs/Dances	Year

Our Family's Favorite Entertainers

When we're asked to name our favorite stars of the entertainment world, a host of talented men and women crowd into our minds. We remember with gratitude the incredible grace of Mikhail Baryshnikov and Fred Astaire, and the jokes and antics of Charlie Chaplin, W. C. Fields, Jack Benny, Lucille Ball, Carol Burnett and the Muppets.

Katherine Hepburn, Spencer Tracy, Bette Davis and Cary Grant will never be forgotten, nor will the voices and the music of Beverly Sills, Luciano Pavorotti, Barbra Streisand, Ella Fitzgerald, Bing Crosby, Frank Sinatra, Louis Armstrong, Elvis Presley, Bennie Goodman and the Beatles.

When you and your family list the names of your favorite stars, you will recall with pleasure the men and women who brought so much laughter and sheer enjoyment into your lives.

Name	Profession	Occasion

Name	Profession	Occasion

Our Favorite Dishes and Recipes

Never before have the people of this country been offered such an incredible variety of dishes, delicacies and culinary styles. Today, there are restaurants and cookbooks that give us the opportunity to enjoy the favorite dishes of every nation in the world and to taste the masterpieces of its famous chefs.

In your kitchen, you are the master creative chef so on these pages you will have the opportunity to describe the favorite dishes of the different members of your family, and to write about your own recipes, menus and culinary delights.

Name _____

Recipe _____

Ingredients _____

_____

_____

_____

Comments _____

_____

_____

_____

_____

Name _____

Recipe _____

Ingredients _____

_____

_____

_____

Comments _____

_____

_____

_____

Name _____

Recipe _____

Ingredients _____

_____

_____

_____

Comments _____

_____

_____

_____

_____

Name _____

Recipe _____

Ingredients _____

_____

_____

_____

Comments _____

_____

_____

_____

Name _____

Recipe _____

Ingredients _____

_____

_____

_____

Comments _____

_____

_____

_____

_____

Name _____

Recipe _____

Ingredients _____

_____

_____

_____

Comments _____

_____

_____

_____

_____

Name _____

Recipe _____

Ingredients _____

_____

_____

_____

Comments _____

_____

_____

_____

Name _____

Recipe _____

Ingredients _____

_____

_____

_____

Comments _____

_____

_____

_____

_____

Name _____

Recipe _____

Ingredients _____

_____

_____

_____

Comments _____

_____

_____

_____

_____

Name _____

Recipe _____

Ingredients _____

_____

_____

_____

Comments _____

_____

_____

_____

Name _____
Recipe _____
Ingredients _____

_____

_____

Comments _____

_____

_____

_____

Name _____
Recipe _____
Ingredients _____

_____

_____

Comments _____

_____

_____

_____

Name _____
Recipe _____
Ingredients _____

_____

_____

Comments _____

_____

_____

Name _____
Recipe _____
Ingredients _____

_____

_____

Comments _____

_____

_____

_____

Name _____
Recipe _____
Ingredients _____

_____

_____

Comments _____

_____

_____

_____

Name _____
Recipe _____
Ingredients _____

_____

_____

Comments _____

_____

_____

Name ....

Recipe ....

Ingredients ....

....

....

....

Comments ....

....

....

....

....

Name ....

Recipe ....

Ingredients ....

....

....

....

Comments ....

....

....

....

....

Name ....

Recipe ....

Ingredients ....

....

....

Comments ....

....

....

Name ....

Recipe ....

Ingredients ....

....

....

....

Comments ....

....

....

....

....

Name ....

Recipe ....

Ingredients ....

....

....

....

Comments ....

....

....

....

....

Name ....

Recipe ....

Ingredients ....

....

....

Comments ....

....

....

Name

Recipe

Ingredients

Comments

Name

Recipe

Ingredients

Comments

Name

Recipe

Ingredients

Comments

Name

Recipe

Ingredients

Comments

Name

Recipe

Ingredients

Comments

Name

Recipe

Ingredients

Comments

Our Family's Achievements, Awards and Honors

In the preceding chapters of this book, you have described many of your family's achievements and records in education, sport, business, profession, military service and public life. On these pages, you have the opportunity of selecting the most memorable and important of these accomplishments and writing about them in greater detail.

These pages will then be a meaningful record of achievement or the living Honor Roll of your family and of your ancestors.

Name	Achievement	Date

Name	Achievement	Date

The Medical History of Our Family

These pages provide an appropriate place to record your family's illnesses, injuries and operations as well as their blood types, dates of immunizations and inoculations, reactions to various treatments and drugs, etc. Recording this information for future reference can be very helpful for your immediate family, and it might be extremely beneficial for future generations. As you know, heredity plays an important part in the transference of susceptibility or resistance to certain diseases and malfunctions.

Name _____ Date of Birth _____ Blood Type _____

Major Illness _____ Date _____ Attending Doctor _____

Hospital _____ City _____ State _____

Prescription Medication _____ Doctor _____

Ailment _____ Date _____ To Date _____

Comments _____

_____

_____

_____

_____

Name _____ Date of Birth _____ Blood Type _____

Major Illness _____ Date _____ Attending Doctor _____

Hospital _____ City _____ State _____

Prescription Medication _____ Doctor _____

Ailment _____ Date _____ To Date _____

Comments _____

_____

_____

_____

Name _____ Date of Birth _____ Blood Type _____
Major Illness _____ Date _____ Attending Doctor _____
Hospital _____ City _____ State _____
Prescription Medication _____ Doctor _____
Ailment _____ Date _____ To Date _____
Comments _____
_____

Name _____ Date of Birth _____ Blood Type _____
Major Illness _____ Date _____ Attending Doctor _____
Hospital _____ City _____ State _____
Prescription Medication _____ Doctor _____
Ailment _____ Date _____ To Date _____
Comments _____
_____

Name _____ Date of Birth _____ Blood Type _____
Major Illness _____ Date _____ Attending Doctor _____
Hospital _____ City _____ State _____
Prescription Medication _____ Doctor _____
Ailment _____ Date _____ To Date _____
Comments _____
_____

Name _____ Date of Birth _____ Blood Type _____
Major Illness _____ Date _____ Attending Doctor _____
Hospital _____ City _____ State _____
Prescription Medication _____ Doctor _____
Ailment _____ Date _____ To Date _____
Comments _____
_____

Name _____ Date of Birth _____ Blood Type _____
Major Illness _____ Date _____ Attending Doctor _____
Hospital _____ City _____ State _____
Prescription Medication _____ Doctor _____
Ailment _____ Date _____ To Date _____
Comments _____
_____
_____

Name _____ Date of Birth _____ Blood Type _____
Major Illness _____ Date _____ Attending Doctor _____
Hospital _____ City _____ State _____
Prescription Medication _____ Doctor _____
Ailment _____ Date _____ To Date _____
Comments _____
_____
_____

Name _____ Date of Birth _____ Blood Type _____
Major Illness _____ Date _____ Attending Doctor _____
Hospital _____ City _____ State _____
Prescription Medication _____ Doctor _____
Ailment _____ Date _____ To Date _____
Comments _____
_____
_____

Name _____ Date of Birth _____ Blood Type _____
Major Illness _____ Date _____ Attending Doctor _____
Hospital _____ City _____ State _____
Prescription Medication _____ Doctor _____
Ailment _____ Date _____ To Date _____
Comments _____
_____

Name _____ Date of Birth _____ Blood Type _____
Major Illness _____ Date _____ Attending Doctor _____
Hospital _____ City _____ State _____
Prescription Medication _____ Doctor _____
Ailment _____ Date _____ To Date _____
Comments _____
_____
_____

Name _____ Date of Birth _____ Blood Type _____
Major Illness _____ Date _____ Attending Doctor _____
Hospital _____ City _____ State _____
Prescription Medication _____ Doctor _____
Ailment _____ Date _____ To Date _____
Comments _____
_____
_____

Name _____ Date of Birth _____ Blood Type _____
Major Illness _____ Date _____ Attending Doctor _____
Hospital _____ City _____ State _____
Prescription Medication _____ Doctor _____
Ailment _____ Date _____ To Date _____
Comments _____
_____
_____

Name _____ Date of Birth _____ Blood Type _____
Major Illness _____ Date _____ Attending Doctor _____
Hospital _____ City _____ State _____
Prescription Medication _____ Doctor _____
Ailment _____ Date _____ To Date _____
Comments _____
_____

Name _____ Date of Birth _____ Blood Type _____

Major Illness _____ Date _____ Attending Doctor _____

Hospital _____ City _____ State _____

Prescription Medication _____ Doctor _____

Ailment _____ Date _____ To Date _____

Comments _____

_____

Name _____ Date of Birth _____ Blood Type _____

Major Illness _____ Date _____ Attending Doctor _____

Hospital _____ City _____ State _____

Prescription Medication _____ Doctor _____

Ailment _____ Date _____ To Date _____

Comments _____

_____

Name _____ Date of Birth _____ Blood Type _____

Major Illness _____ Date _____ Attending Doctor _____

Hospital _____ City _____ State _____

Prescription Medication _____ Doctor _____

Ailment _____ Date _____ To Date _____

Comments _____

_____

Name _____ Date of Birth _____ Blood Type _____

Major Illness _____ Date _____ Attending Doctor _____

Hospital _____ City _____ State _____

Prescription Medication _____ Doctor _____

Ailment _____ Date _____ To Date _____

Comments _____

_____

Name _____ Date of Birth _____ Blood Type _____

Major Illness _____ Date _____ Attending Doctor _____

Hospital _____ City _____ State _____

Prescription Medication _____ Doctor _____

Ailment _____ Date _____ To Date _____

Comments _____

_____

Name _____ Date of Birth _____ Blood Type _____

Major Illness _____ Date _____ Attending Doctor _____

Hospital _____ City _____ State _____

Prescription Medication _____ Doctor _____

Ailment _____ Date _____ To Date _____

Comments _____

_____

Name _____ Date of Birth _____ Blood Type _____

Major Illness _____ Date _____ Attending Doctor _____

Hospital _____ City _____ State _____

Prescription Medication _____ Doctor _____

Ailment _____ Date _____ To Date _____

Comments _____

_____

Name _____ Date of Birth _____ Blood Type _____

Major Illness _____ Date _____ Attending Doctor _____

Hospital _____ City _____ State _____

Prescription Medication _____ Doctor _____

Ailment _____ Date _____ To Date _____

Comments _____

_____

Name _____ Date of Birth _____ Blood Type _____

Major Illiness _____ Date _____ Attending Doctor _____

Hospital _____ City _____ State _____

Prescription Medication _____ Doctor _____

Ailment _____ Date _____ To Date _____

Comments _____

_____

_____

Name _____ Date of Birth _____ Blood Type _____

Major Illiness _____ Date _____ Attending Doctor _____

Hospital _____ City _____ State _____

Prescription Medication _____ Doctor _____

Ailment _____ Date _____ To Date _____

Comments _____

_____

_____

Name _____ Date of Birth _____ Blood Type _____

Major Illiness _____ Date _____ Attending Doctor _____

Hospital _____ City _____ State _____

Prescription Medication _____ Doctor _____

Ailment _____ Date _____ To Date _____

Comments _____

_____

_____

Name _____ Date of Birth _____ Blood Type _____

Major Illiness _____ Date _____ Attending Doctor _____

Hospital _____ City _____ State _____

Prescription Medication _____ Doctor _____

Ailment _____ Date _____ To Date _____

Comments _____

_____

Name _____ Date of Birth _____ Blood Type _____
Major Illiness _____ Date _____ Attending Doctor _____
Hospital _____ City _____ State _____
Prescription Medication _____ Doctor _____
Ailment _____ Date _____ To Date _____
Comments _____
_____

Name _____ Date of Birth _____ Blood Type _____
Major Illiness _____ Date _____ Attending Doctor _____
Hospital _____ City _____ State _____
Prescription Medication _____ Doctor _____
Ailment _____ Date _____ To Date _____
Comments _____
_____

Name _____ Date of Birth _____ Blood Type _____
Major Illiness _____ Date _____ Attending Doctor _____
Hospital _____ City _____ State _____
Prescription Medication _____ Doctor _____
Ailment _____ Date _____ To Date _____
Comments _____
_____

Name _____ Date of Birth _____ Blood Type _____
Major Illiness _____ Date _____ Attending Doctor _____
Hospital _____ City _____ State _____
Prescription Medication _____ Doctor _____
Ailment _____ Date _____ To Date _____
Comments _____

Name _____ Date of Birth _____ Blood Type _____

Major Illiness _____ Date _____ Attending Doctor _____

Hospital _____ City _____ State _____

Prescription Medication _____ Doctor _____

Ailment _____ Date _____ To Date _____

Comments _____

_____

_____

Name _____ Date of Birth _____ Blood Type _____

Major Illiness _____ Date _____ Attending Doctor _____

Hospital _____ City _____ State _____

Prescription Medication _____ Doctor _____

Ailment _____ Date _____ To Date _____

Comments _____

_____

_____

Name _____ Date of Birth _____ Blood Type _____

Major Illiness _____ Date _____ Attending Doctor _____

Hospital _____ City _____ State _____

Prescription Medication _____ Doctor _____

Ailment _____ Date _____ To Date _____

Comments _____

_____

_____

Name _____ Date of Birth _____ Blood Type _____

Major Illiness _____ Date _____ Attending Doctor _____

Hospital _____ City _____ State _____

Prescription Medication _____ Doctor _____

Ailment _____ Date _____ To Date _____

Comments _____

_____

_____

Name _____ Date of Birth _____ Blood Type _____

Major Illness _____ Date _____ Attending Doctor _____

Hospital _____ City _____ State _____

Prescription Medication _____ Doctor _____

Ailment _____ Date _____ To Date _____

Comments _____

_____

_____

Name _____ Date of Birth _____ Blood Type _____

Major Illness _____ Date _____ Attending Doctor _____

Hospital _____ City _____ State _____

Prescription Medication _____ Doctor _____

Ailment _____ Date _____ To Date _____

Comments _____

_____

_____

Name _____ Date of Birth _____ Blood Type _____

Major Illness _____ Date _____ Attending Doctor _____

Hospital _____ City _____ State _____

Prescription Medication _____ Doctor _____

Ailment _____ Date _____ To Date _____

Comments _____

_____

_____

Name _____ Date of Birth _____ Blood Type _____

Major Illness _____ Date _____ Attending Doctor _____

Hospital _____ City _____ State _____

Prescription Medication _____ Doctor _____

Ailment _____ Date _____ To Date _____

Comments _____

_____

_____

Sources of Ancestral Records in Europe

continued from page 33

Copies of other legal documents, tax returns, deeds, military service records, etc., can be obtained by writing:

Public Record Office
Ruskin Avenue, Kew, Richmond
Surrey TW 9 4DU, England

If you need the services of a professional research person, write to this organization:

The Society of Genealogists
37 Harrinton Gardens
London SW 7 4JX, England

RECOMMENDED GUIDES:

Burke's Family Index, *Burke's Peerage, London, 1976.*

Burke's Landed Gentry, *Burke's Peerage, London, 1972.*

Descriptive Inventory of the English Collection, Genealogical Society of Utah *by Arthur Eakle, Heribert Hinricks, Richard S. Tompkins and Arvilla Outsen, University of Utah, Salt Lake City, Utah, 1979.*

English Family Research *by J. Konrad, Summit Publications, Munroe Falls, Ohio, 1979.*

Genealogical Handbook for England and Wales *by Joseph Hall, Gregory Inn, Salt Lake City, Utah, 1977.*

Genealogical Research in England and Wales *by David C. Gardner and Frank Smith, Bookcraft Publishers, Salt Lake City, Utah, 1962.*

Handy Guide to English Genealogical Records *by Phyllis P. Preece and Floren S. Preece, Everton Publishers, Logan, Utah, 1978.*

Major Genealogical Sources in England and Wales. *LDS Series A, Nos. 3-53, Genealogical Society of Utah, Salt Lake City, Utah.*

Genealogy for Beginners *by A. J. Willis, Genealogical Publishing Society, Baltimore, Maryland, 1970.*

Estonia

See Russia (Union of Soviet Socialist Republics).

Finland

Registrations of births, marriages and deaths are the responsibility of ecclesiastical authorities who are predominantly of the Evangelic Lutheran Church. Other denominations include the Greek Orthodox and Moslem faiths.

For most parish records, write to the Kirkhoherranverasto (Church Minister's Office) of the Civilregistermyndighet (Civil Register Authorities) in the town where your ancestor lived. Parish registers earlier than 1850 are kept in the National Archives. The address:

Valtionarkisto/Riksarkivet
PL 274, SF 00171
Helsinki 17
Finland

The Central Archives of the Lutheran Church are located in Helsinki:

Suomen Lutherilaisen
Evankeliumiyhdistyksen
Kirjasto
Malmink 12B
SF 00100 Helsinki
Finland

The Archives of the Ecclesiastical Board of the Finnish Orthodox Church are located at Kuopio:

Suomen Orthodoksinen
Kirkollishallitus Orthodoxa
Kyrkistyrelsen,
Puistokatu 35
703000 Kuopio 30
Finland

France

Many genealogists believe that the records of France are the most well-organized in Europe. Registries of births, marriages and deaths dating to the 17th century were kept in the parishes. In 1791, these church records were declared to be civil records and *were transferred to the Regional Archives. Churches continue to register vital statistics in duplicate, keeping one copy and sending the other to the Regional Archives. The mayor (maire) also makes duplicates of records, keeping one in the town hall (hôtel de ville) and sending one to the Regional Archives.*

A highly informative newsletter from the French Embassy states: "There is no central office in France keeping records for the entire country. Therefore, in order to trace one's family roots, one must have the name of the place of origin in France."

The letter then lists the names and addresses of the ninety-six Archives Départmentales in France. You can obtain a copy of this invaluable letter by writing or phoning your nearest French Consulate General or the Embassy in Washington:

> *The French Embassy*
> *2535 Belmont Road, N.W.*
> *Washington, D C 20008*

Take every means to make sure of the spelling of your ancestor's name, the approximate date of his or her birth, marriage or death and his or her place of origin. Then send your request to the Archives Départementales (Regional Archives) nearest to your ancestor's town. The letter from the French Embassy suggests: "A typed letter, in French, will greatly improve the chances of receiving an answer, provided one includes a self-addressed envelope together with two International Reply coupons which can be purchased at any Post Office."

The Regional Archives also store the census indexes which have been taken at five-year intervals since 1936.

The documents in the National Archives are a delight to genealogists. They have feudal records dating from 1050 to 1700, probate and land records going back to 1300, military records from 1600, immigration records which go back to 1686. The address:

> *Archives Nationale de France*
> *60 Rue des Francs-Bourgeois*
> *75141 Paris CEDEX 03*

RECOMMENDED GUIDES:

***Preliminary Survey of the French Collection, Genealogical Society of Utah** by C. Russell Jensen, University of Utah, Salt Lake City, Utah, 1978.*

***Major Genealogical Record Sources in France,** Series G, No. 1, Genealogical Society of Utah, Salt Lake City, Utah.*

***Genealogy: An Introduction to Continental Concepts,** Polyanthos, New Orleans, Louisiana, 1976.*

***French Genealogist,** Augustan Society, Torrance, California, 1977.*

Germany

It is helpful to know something of the history of the country in which you are tracing your ancestors. This is particularly true of Germany.

In the 18th century, such countries as England, France, Spain and Sweden had been politically unified nations for hundreds of years, while the vast territory known as Germany was made up of a patchwork of more than three hundred kingdoms, principalities and dukedoms.

The Napoleonic Wars and the Treaty of Vienna served to merge some of these states, and by the mid-19th century, the thirty larger states had absorbed their smaller neighbors through wars, alliances and political marriages. A yearning for nationalism swept through Germany, and at the end of the Franco-Prussian War in 1871, King Wilhelm I of Prussia, was proclaimed Emperor of Germany.

After World War II, Germany was divided into the Federal Republic of Germany (West Germany) and the German Democratic Republic (East Germany). West Germany consists of the historic states of Baden, Bavaria, Hanover, Hesse, the Rhineland, Schlewswig-Holstein and Westphalia. East Germany consists of Brandenburg, Brunswick, Mecklenburg, Saxony and Thuringia.

Germany's turbulent history has prevented the establishment of a single centralized source of vital statistics. Instead, there are many well-organized, localized records agencies. Maralyn Wellauer's **A Guide to Genealogical Research** (see Bibliography) lists 35 State Archives, 131 Town Archives and 35 Church Archives in West Germany, as well as 15 State Archives, 36 Town Archives and 4 Church Archives in East Germany. Also listed are 53 genealogical societies in West Germany.

When you have established an ancestor's identity (his or her correct name, place and approximate date of residence), there's a good chance that you may find many interesting records relating to him or her.

Prior to 1876, births, marriages and deaths were registered by the churches and communities of the various religious denominations. Since 1876, these vital statistics have been recorded and filed at the Standesamt (civil registry office) in the city, town or village where the event occurred. The address in West Germany:

> Standesamt
> (Name of city, town or village)
> Bundesrepublik
> Deutschland

The address in East Germany is:

> Standesamt
> (Name of city, town or village)
> Deutsch Demokratische Republik

Of great importance are the emigration records for the Hamburg-Kiel area which are stored in the State Archives of Hamburg. The staff will search passenger lists for an hourly fee. The address:

> Staatsarchiv
> Rathaus Markt 1
> 2000 Hamburg,
> Bundesrepublik
> Deutschland

The Genealogical Society's Library in Utah has microfilms of these passenger lists, which you can view in their branch libraries.

RECOMMENDED GUIDES:

The Atlantic Bridge to Germany by Charles M. Hall, Everton Publishers, Logan, Utah, 1978.

German Family Research Made Simple by J. Konrad, Summit Publications, Inc., Monroe Falls, Ohio, 1977.

A Genealogical Handbook of German Research by Larry D. Jensen, Pleasant Grove, Utah.

How to Find My German Ancestors by Dr. Heinz F. Frederichs, Neustadt, Germany, 1969.

Preliminary Survey of the German Collection, Genealogical Society of Utah by Ronald Smelser with Thomas Dullien, University of Utah, Salt Lake City, Utah, 1979.

Searching for German Ancestors: East Germany, West Germany by Virginia Eschenbach, Genealogical Helper, Logan, Utah, 1976.

Historical Background Affecting Genealogical Research in Germany and Austria, Series C, No. 19, Genealogical Society of Utah, Salt Lake City, Utah.

Tracing Your German Roots by M. A. Wellauer, 3239 N. 58th Street, Milwaukee, Wisconsin, 1978.

A Genealogical Handbook of German Research by L. O. Jensen and N. J. Storrer, P. O. Box 502, Pleasant Grove, Utah, 1977.

Encyclopedia of German-American Research by C. N. and Anna P.-C. Smith, R. R. Bowker Co., New York, New York, 1976.

Greece

During the turbulent history of Greece, the registering of births, marriages and deaths has been highly irregular. Before 1925, records were kept by the various religious denominations, and it is hoped that they can still be found in their files.

Civil registrations became mandatory in 1925. Certificates of vital statistics are now kept by special registration offices in the cities of Athens, Piraeus and Salonika. In other cities, towns and communities, they are registered and filed by the mayors or by the presidents of communities.

For further information about civil registration, write the central Recording Office or the National Statistical Service at these addresses:

> Recording Office
> Ministry of the Interior
> 57 Panepistimous Avenue
> Athens, Greece

> National Statistical Service
> 14–16 Lykourgou Street
> Athens, Greece

Marriage certificates are issued and filed by the metropolitan in each district. You might write to the office of the Archbishop to find out the proper metropolitan to write for a marriage certificate and for information about pre-1925 vital statistics' records filed in Orthodox churches.

> Greek Orthodox Archdiocese
> 21 Aghias Filotheis
> Athens, Greece

Hungary

Before World War I, Hungary was one of the largest countries in Europe. At the conclusion of the war, the Versailles Treaty in 1918 assigned parts of Hungary to Czechoslovakia, Yugoslavia, the Soviet Union and Romania. If your ancestors lived in any of these regions before World War I, their records are probably stored in the National Archives in Budapest. The address is shown below.

Before 1895, records of vital statistics were registered by the various religious denominations. Requests for copies of these older documents should be sent to the appropriate church or religious community in the town of your ancestor.

In 1895, the government ordered that vital statistics' records were to be registered and kept by local municipal offices. In 1918, all these records were gathered in the National Center of Archives in Budapest. These records, plus all those registered from 1918 to today, are kept at the National Center of Archives at this address:

> Leveltarak Orszagos Kozpontja
> Uri Utca 54–56
> Budapest 1, Hungary

Also included in the Archives' files are the 1895-to-1918 vital statistics' records of those regions of Czechoslovakia, Yugoslavia, the Soviet Union and Romania which were a part of pre-World War I Hungary.

Luckily for us, the Mormon Genealogical Society has microfilms of the National Center of Archives' records which, like all their films, can be studied at the Main Library and the Branch Libraries.

RECOMMENDED GUIDES:

Handy Guide to Hungarian General Records by Jared H. Suess, Everton Publishers, Logan, Utah, 1980.

Hungarian Genealogical Dictionary by Larry Jensen, Saskatchewan Genealogical Society, Regina, Saskatchewan, Canada, 1975.

Ireland

People seeking information about their ancestors in Ireland are sometimes hindered by the destruction of records in fires which severely damaged government buildings in 1882, 1916 and 1922. However, the history of your ancestors is well documented.

When tracing an ancestor in Ireland, first write to the Registrar General in Dublin and request the special forms needed to initiate a search for records of birth, marriage and death. To fill out the form, you'll need the ancestor's name, place of birth or death, approximate date of birth or death, and his or her occupation. The offices' files include vital statistics' records since 1864, and the staff will conduct a search for an hourly fee. The address:

> The Office of the Registrar General
> The Customs House
> Dublin 1, The Republic of Ireland

In the Public Records Office are filed books of all property owners and tenants during the first half of the 19th century, abstracts of wills, indexes to wills, Protestant marriage license bonds, etc. The address: Deputy Keeper, Public Records Office, Four Courts Building, Dublin 1.

In the Registry of Deeds are records dating

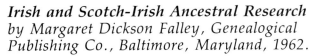

back to 1701 which cover property transactions involving deeds, leases, mortgages, business agreements, wills, etc. The address: The Registry of Deeds, Henrietta Street, Dublin 1.

The Genealogical Offices have an outstanding collection of documents, records, manuscripts, family histories and armorial bearings dating back to the 16th century. To request a genealogical search, you should first send for Form B which asks for information about your family. The staff will then conduct research on your behalf for a set hourly fee. The address: The Genealogical Offices, Dublin Castle, Dublin 1.

The National Library houses fine collections of manuscripts, books, family histories, old newspaper files, old family papers, microfilms of parish books (1848–1864), etc. The address: The National Library and Archives, Kildare Street, Dublin 2.

Among the collections of the State Paper Office are convict and criminal index books, registers of convicts sentenced to transportation and servitude, the 1798 Rebellion papers, proceedings of the United Irishmen, Fenians, Land League, etc. The address: The State Paper Office, Birmingham Tower, Dublin Castle, Dublin 1.

Parish registers are a rewarding source of vital statistics and of personal notes added by the parish priests. The Irish Catholic Directory, published annually, lists all the parishes and their priests for both the Republic of Ireland and Northern Ireland. When you determine your ancestor's parish, write the priest and request that he examine his registers for any information about your forefathers. He probably will be familiar with such requests. A gratuity of two pounds is customary.

RECOMMENDED GUIDES:

Handbook on Irish Genealogy, Heraldic Artists, Dublin, Ireland, 1973.

Irish Family Research Made Simple by E. J. Collins, Summit Publications, Inc., Munroe Falls, Ohio, 1980.

Irish Research and Sources by Betty L. McCoy, Indianapolis, Indiana, 1972.

Irish and Scotch-Irish Ancestral Research by Margaret Dickson Falley, Genealogical Publishing Co., Baltimore, Maryland, 1962.

Major Genealogical Sources in Ireland, Series A, No. 2, Genealogical Society of Utah, Salt Lake City, Utah.

A Primer for Irish Genealogical Research by W. R. Ward, Everton Publishers, Logan, Utah, 1977.

Your Irish Ancestors by J. A. Black, Paddington Press, London, 1974.

Israel

For people seeking information about their Jewish ancestors in Europe, the libraries and archives in Israel are prime sources of genealogical records and materials of all kinds. At this time, the archivists and librarians are deeply involved in the monumental task of evaluating, cataloging and filing vast amounts of historical and genealogical materials from all countries of the world. They are not staffed to handle requests by mail although they might be willing to do so. If you have specific and accurate information about an ancestor, you can request a search for which you will be charged a fee.

The Central Archives have a fine collection of materials:

Central Archives for the History of the
    Jewish People
Sprinzak Building
Hebrew University (Givat Ram
    Campus)
P.O. Box 1140
Jerusalem, Israel

In these Archives are collections of manuscripts, vital statistics, records, synagogue and community registers, indexes and communal histories, etc., dating from the 21st century to the present. There are microfilms of more than 3,000,000 documents in their files. Indexes outlining the Archives' contents can be found in the Jewish libraries of this country and in the Mormon Library in Utah.

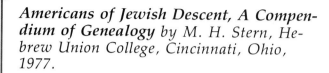

*Jewish National and University
Library
Hebrew University (Givat Ram
Campus)
Jerusalem, Israel*

The archives section of the library has an extensive collection of communal histories and vital statistics registers from all of the European countries. Their registers cover communities in Russia, Germany, Poland, Lithuania, etc.

*Diaspora Research Institute
Tel Aviv University
Tel Aviv, Israel*

In the Institute's files are Jewish individuals and communal histories in Hungary, Romania, Bessarabia and Italy.

*Archives of the Sephardic Community
Hahavazelet Street 12a
Jerusalem, Israel*

These Archives house a varied collection of materials from Eastern Sephardic communities in Palestine, Greece, Turkey and North Africa. These materials include old manuscripts, wills, contracts, tax lists, etc.

*Yad Vashem
Har Hazikarn
P.O. Box 84
Jerusalem, Israel*

The archives of this museum contain personal information on the six million Jewish victims of the Holocaust. Also being filed are the records and histories of hundreds of Jewish communities. It is hoped that the archives will be able to answer requests by mail in the near future.

RECOMMENDED GUIDES:

Finding Our Fathers, A Guidebook to Jewish Genealogy by Dan Rottenberg, Random House, New York, 1977.

From Generation to Generation, by Arthur Kurzweil, William Morrow and Co., Inc., New York, 1918.

Americans of Jewish Descent, Sources of Information for Tracing Their Genealogy by M. H. Stern, National Genealogical Society, Washington, D.C., 1958.

Americans of Jewish Descent, A Compendium of Genealogy by M. H. Stern, Hebrew Union College, Cincinnati, Ohio, 1977.

Italy

The records in Italy's municipal and church registries are among the most voluminous and ancient in Europe. Unfortunately, the filing systems for seldom-used documents are often irregular, and it is difficult to obtain copies of birth, marriage and death records by mail. Such records have not been gathered into central files.

Since 1851, records of vital statistics have been kept in municipal registries. In Rome they are stored in the Central Bureau of Statistics:

*Instituto Centrale de Statistica
Via Balbo 16
1-100044 Rome, Italy*

For records in other communities, write to the local office of Vital Statistics:

*Ufficio di Stato Civil
1-(Name of city or town), Italy*

The National Archives in Rome has an impressive collection of genealogical documents and manuscripts. The address:

*Archiva Centrale della Strato
Corso Rinnascimento 40
Rome, Italy*

State Archives are located in the following cities: Bologna, Florence, Lucca, Naples, Pisa, Rome, Trieste and Venice.

Italy is famous for its fine libraries which have extensive genealogical divisions. In Rome there is the Vatican Library, the Biblioteca Nazionale, the Biblioteca Vittorio Emmanuele, Biblioteca Angelica and Biblioteca Casanatense. Other outstanding libraries are the Biblioteca Mediceo-Laurentiana in Florence, the University Library in Bologna, the Royal Library of Modena, the Ambrosiana in Milan, the Library of Parma and the Biblioteca Marciana in Venice.

RECOMMENDED GUIDES:

Handy Guide to Italian Genealogical Records by Phyllis P. Preece and Floren S. Preece, Everton Publishers, Logan, Utah, 1978.

Major Genealogical Records Sources in Italy, Series G, No. 2, Genealogical Society of Utah, Salt Lake City, Utah.

Italian Genealogist, Augustan Society, Torrance, California, 1977.

Latvia and Lithuania

See Russia (**Union of Soviet Socialist Republics**).

The Netherlands

In their orderly fashion, the Dutch have established a **Central Bureau for Genealogy** connected with their National Archives. The address:

> Central Bureau of Genealogy
> P.O. Box 1175
> 2502 AP The Hague
> The Netherlands

This Bureau has published a well-organized book entitled "Searching for Your Ancestors in the Netherlands" which you can obtain from the above address for a $4 fee.

Copies of birth, marriage and death certificates are stored at the municipal level. Copies are available for a fee of $4. Address your requests as follows:

> Civil Registry
> City Hall
> (Name of town or city),
> The Netherlands

RECOMMENDED GUIDES:

Major Genealogical Sources in the Netherlands, Series C, Nos. 3, 5–15, Genealogical Society of Utah, Salt Lake City, Utah.

Be-Ne-Lux Genealogist, Augustan Society, Torrance, California, 1977.

Northern Ireland

Copies of certificates of births, marriages and deaths since 1922 can be obtained by writing:

> Registrar General
> Oxford House, Chichester Street
> Belfast, BT1 4HL, Northern Ireland

At this date, the fee for a copy of a certificate is £2.40p. which includes airmail reply.

Records prior to 1922 are kept at the General Register Office in the Republic of Ireland. The address:

> General Register Office
> Customs House
> Dublin, Republic of Ireland

Copies of divorce decrees can be obtained by writing:

> Chief Registrar, High Court of Justice
> in Northern Ireland
> Principal Registry
> Royal Courts of Justice, Chichester
> Street
> Belfast, BT1 3JF, Northern Ireland

Wills are kept for twenty years at the following office:

> Principal Probate Registry
> Royal Courts of Justice
> Belfast, BT1 3JF, Northern Ireland

Copies of wills more than twenty years old and other documents (deeds, property registers, tax returns, etc.) can be obtained at this office:

> Public Record Office
> 66 Balmoral Avenue
> Belfast, BT9 6NY, Northern Ireland

The Public Record Office no longer undertakes genealogical research. If you need such services, write to the Ulster Historical Foundation whose offices are also at the above address.

RECOMMENDED GUIDES:

Irish and Scotch-Irish Ancestral Research by Margaret Dickson Folley, Genealogical Publishing Company, Baltimore, Maryland, 1962.

Scotch-Irish Family Research Made Simple by R. G. Campbell, Summit Publications, Inc., Munroe Falls, Ohio, 1974.

Norway

If you are seeking information about your Norwegian ancestors, your first step is quite simple. Write to the Norwegian Embassy or to the nearest Consulate General and request their excellent booklet prepared by the Royal Norwegian Ministry of Foreign Affairs, entitled "How to Trace Your Ancestors in Norway." The Embassy is located at this address:

Norwegian Embassy
3401 Massachusetts Avenue NW
Washington, D C 20007

This booklet describes the many sources of information about Norwegian ancestry in this country: official agencies, Norwegian associations, genealogical societies, etc. It is essential that you have accurate information about your immigrating ancestors (names, dates and places).

This is particularly true in the Scandinavian countries where hereditary surnames were not adopted until the late 19th century. Children had previously taken their father's given name as a surname by adding -sen, -son or -datter. Therefore, succeeding generations in each family had different surnames. To further complicate matters, some people took the name of the farm which they owned or on which they worked. So a farm-laborer's family might have the same name as the farm-owner although they were not related in any way. If a laborer moved to another farm, he then took the name of his new employer.

"How to Trace Your Ancestors in Norway" explains this surname situation in detail. It then outlines the sources of statistical and personal information in Norway: the National Archives, the Regional Archives, parish registers, census returns (dating back to 1769), probate registers (dating back to 1660), registers of conveyances and mortgages, real estate registers, immigrant records, emigrant lists, court records, military records, etc.

RECOMMENDED GUIDES:

Genealogical Guidebook and Atlas of Norway by Frank Smith and Finn A. Thomsen, Everton Publishers, Logan, Utah, 1978.

Norwegian Family History and Research, Series D, Nos. 11–13, 20–24, Genealogical Society of Utah, Salt Lake City, Utah.

Tracing Your Norwegian Roots by Maralyn A. Wellauer, 3239 North 58th St., Milwaukee, Wisconsin, 1979.

Poland

The history of long-suffering Poland is the most turbulent of all the European nations. In 1771, Poland had the largest land area of any country in Europe. Then its three neighbors, Russia, Prussia and Austria, took advantage of Poland's internal problems and in three partitions totally dismembered the country. By 1795, Poland ceased to exist as a self-governing country.

But the Polish people's love of liberty never faltered, and they continued to resist their invaders. Finally in 1918, Poland once more became an independent nation after World War I. Their freedom was short-lived. In the aftermath of World War II, Poland was forced to become a People's Republic in the sphere of the Soviet Union. For people seeking information about their ancestors, this means that the availability of genealogical records depends on the state of affairs existing between the USSR and the rest of the world.

We are informed that the most effective methods of obtaining vital statistics records is to travel to Poland and conduct your own on-the-spot research or to employ the services of professional research people in Poland. You can probably learn the names and addresses of such individuals through your local Polish associations, alliances, genealogical societies, etc.

The U.S. Embassy in Warsaw will try to obtain copies of birth, marriage and death records if you send them the name of your

ancestor and the date and place of the event. Write to this address:

> United States Embassy in Warsaw
> c/o Department of State
> Washington, D C 20521

Following is an outline of the official sources of vital statistics records. Records of births, marriages and deaths have traditionally been kept by the churches. Civil registration began in 1870.

Records of vital statistics within the city limits of Warsaw are kept in this office:

> Urzad Stanu Cywilnego
> Warzawa-Strodmiecie, Poland

Records in the Praga area are stored in this office:

> Urzad Stanu Cywilnego
> Warzawaw-Praga, Poland

In larger cities and towns outside Warsaw and Praga, records are kept locally:

> Urzad Stanu Cywilnego
> (Name of city or town), Poland

In small towns and villages, records are kept in the communal office:

> Urzad Stanu Cywilnego Gminnej Ray
>   Narodowrj
> (Name of town or village), Poland

There are two National Archives in Warsaw. One stores records which are dated prior to 1918. The address:

> Archiwum Glowne Akt Dawnych
> Dluga 7
> Warsaw, Poland

The other archives hold post-1918 records. The address:

> Archiwum Akt Nowych
> Dluga 7
> Warsaw, Poland

RECOMMENDED GUIDES:

Polish Family Research by J. Konrad, Summit Publications, Munroe Falls, Ohio, 1979.

Polish Family Tree Surnames by T. J. Obal, Hillsdale, New Jersey, 1977.

Tracing Your Polish Roots by Maralyn A. Wellauer, 3239 North 58th St., Milwaukee, Wisconsin, 1979.

Polish Research, Series C, No. 31, Genealogical Society of Utah, Salt Lake City, Utah.

A Genealogical Guide and Atlas of Silesia by O. K. and V. N. Kowallis, Everton Publishers, Logan, Utah, 1976.

Eastern European Genealogist, Augustan Society, Torrance, California, 1977.

Portugal

The parish churches have traditionally kept records of births, marriages and deaths, and they still do so. Civil registration of these events officially began in 1878, and the records are filed in the Office of Civil Registrar of each town or community. When requesting copies of vital statistics' certificates, write to:

> Conservatoria de Registo Civil
> (Name of town) Portugal

After one hundred years, records are transferred to the nearest District Archives.

> Arquivo dos Registros Paroquiais
> Rua dos Prazeres 41 r/c
> Lisboa, Portugal

> Arquivo Nacional da Torre do Tombo
> Palacio da San Bento
> Lisboa, Portugal

> Arquivo Historico Ultramrino
> Calcada da Boa-Hora 30
> Palacio da Ega
> Lisboa, Portugal

> Arquivo Distrital
> Praca da Republica 38
> Porto, Portugal

> Arquivo Distrital
> Largo da Caixa Geral de Despositos
> Leira, Portugal

> Arquivo Distrital
> Rua da Mouraria
> Palacio de Sao Pedro
> Funchal, Madeira, Portugal

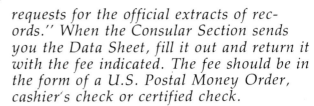

Romania

In 1831, the religious communities of Romania were ordered to keep records of births, marriages and deaths. In 1865, civil registration became mandatory.

To request copies of your ancestor's records, write to the local Office of Vital Statistics of the People's Council.

> *Oficiul Starii Civile Statul Popular*
> *(Name of your ancestor's town)*
> *Romania*

Birth, marriage and death records are kept for seventy-five years and then sent to the state archives. This applies to religious registers as well as civil registers. The State Archives is located at this address:

> *Directia Generala*
> *Archivelor Statuli*
> *B-Dul Gheorghe Gheorghui*
> *Dej nr. 29*
> *Bucharest, Romania*

Russia (Union of Soviet Socialist Republics)

At this time, it is impossible to obtain information about one's ancestor's in Russia by using normal methods of genealogical research. This is also true in Estonia, Latvia and Lithuania which have been annexed by the Soviet Union.

Before the Revolution in 1917, births, marriages and deaths were recorded by the various religious denominations. Since then, these vital statistics have been kept by the local offices of the Ministry of the Interior.

We have been informed that copies of birth, marriage and death certificates can be requested through our State Department. Address your request as follows:

> *Consular Section*
> *American Embassy, Moscow,*
> *c/o Department of State*
> *Washington, D C 20521*

In your letter, state your purpose and ask for ''a Data Sheet which the Soviet Ministry of Foreign Affairs requires to process

requests for the official extracts of records.'' When the Consular Section sends you the Data Sheet, fill it out and return it with the fee indicated. The fee should be in the form of a U.S. Postal Money Order, cashier's check or certified check.

The results have not been encouraging. It takes months to receive a reply which usually states that the document you requested cannot be found. However, as long as there's a chance for success, most ancestor-hunters are willing to risk it.

*Probably the genealogical societies and libraries in this country will be far more rewarding sources of information for you. We also recommend that you consult the nearest Branch Library of the Mormon Genealogical Society. Their extensive files of research papers and microfilms might contain just the information you're looking for. If you're seeking information about a Jewish ancestor in Russia, we suggest you refer to the **Israel** section in this chapter.*

RECOMMENDED GUIDE:

Russian History Atlas *by Martin Gilbert, Macmillan Publishing Co., N.Y., 1972.*

Scotland

Copies of certificates of births, marriages and deaths since 1855 can be obtained by writing to this office:

> *Registrar General*
> *New Register House*
> *Edinburgh EH1 3YT, Scotland*

At this time the fee is £3.65p which includes airmail return. Parish records prior to 1855 are also held at this office.

For divorce decrees, write to this address:

> *Extractor of the Court of Session*
> *Parliament House, Parliament Square*
> *Edinburgh, EH1 1RQ, Scotland*

Copies of wills, deeds, property registers, etc., can be obtained by writing:

> *Scottish Record Office*
> *HM General Register House*
> *Edinburgh, EH1 3YY, Scotland*

This office will answer specific inquiries but will not conduct a search. If you desire, they will recommend a reputable professional record-searcher.

RECOMMENDED GUIDES:

A Genealogical Atlas of Scotland by David E. Gardner, Derek Harland and Frank E. Smith, Bookcraft, Inc., Salt Lake City, Utah, 1962.

In Search of Scottish Ancestry by Gerard Hamilton Edwards, Genealogical Publishing Co., Baltimore, Maryland, 1972.

Introductory Scottish Genealogical Research by Donald Whyte, Featherhall Press Ltd., Edinburgh, Scotland, 1980.

Scotch-Irish Research Made Simple by R. G. Campbell, Summit Publications, Munroe Falls, Ohio, 1978.

Spain

The primary source of vital statistics in Spain are the more than 19,000 parish churches, some of whose registers date beyond 1600. You must first determine your ancestor's town of origin to discover his or her church. All parishes are listed in **The Guidebook of the Spanish Church** which is published by the General Office of Information and Statistics of the Church. Some of the Catholic Diocesan Libraries in this country have this **Guidebook**. If you cannot locate one, write to the Spanish diocese of your ancestor's town. When writing to the parish priest for copies of records, he should be addressed as **Revdo Sr. Cura Parocco.**

If your ancestor lived in Spain during the last one hundred years, you can request copies of his or her vital statistics' certificates from the Juzado Municipal (Municipal Court) in the district of his or her birth.

The archives of Spain are fascinating for anyone interested in genealogy. Of course, one must be able to speak Spanish.

> Instituto Nacional de Estadistica
> Avda. Generalisimo 91
> Madrid 16, Spain

The Archives of the Indies has extensive recordings covering the events when Spain was the great power in the New World.

> Achivo General de Indias
> Seville, Spain

The National Historical Archives has excellent collections of manuscripts and registers of genealogical interest.

> Archivo Historico Nacional
> Calle Serrano 115
> Madrid, Spain

There are also fine collections in the Archives of Aragon (Barcelona), Granada, Seville, Toledo, Valencia and Vallodolid.

RECOMMENDED GUIDES:

Spanish American Genealogical Helper, The Hartwell Company, Harbor City, California, 1972.

Sweden

The Royal Ministry for Foreign Affairs has prepared an informative, well-written booklet entitled ''Tracing Your Swedish Ancestors'' which you can obtain by writing to the nearest Consulate-General or the Royal Swedish Embassy, Watergate 600, 600 New Hampshire Avenue NW, Washington, D.C. 10037.

In its 28 pages, this booklet clearly and concisely describes the best methods for gathering the information in this country which you will need to request the records of your ancestors in Sweden. It then describes the orderly Swedish records system.

In brief, the parishes of the established church has been responsible for keeping vital statistics' records since the early 1700s. Every birth, death, marriage, removal from a parish or entry into it are carefully recorded by the pastor. Records are also kept of individual families; their numbers, occupations, education, etc.

To obtain copies of these records, it is essential that you know the correct spelling of an ancestor's name, his or her place of origin and approximate date of birth. The

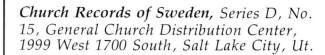

booklet states that if you have this information and if you are persistent, you might be able to trace your Swedish ancestry back two hundred or more years.

After one hundred years, vital statistics' records are transferred to provincial and city archives whose addresses are listed in the booklet and in **Cradled in Sweden** (see Bibliography) which is an excellent guide to Swedish genealogical research. Also listed in this book are the addresses of all the parishes in Sweden.

The Emigrant Institute and the Emigrant Register Office might have records of your ancestors' place of origin. Their addresses:

> Emigrantinstitutet
> P.O. Box 201
> S-351 04 Vaxjo, Sweden.

> Emigrantregistret
> P.O. Box 331
> Sta Kyrkogatan 4,
> S-651 05 Karlstad, Sweden.

The National Archives of Sweden is one of the most well-organized in Europe:

> Riksarkivet
> Arkivatan 3
> Stockholm, Sweden.

Some people seeking information about their Swedish ancestors encounter a problem involving their forefathers' names. It was not until the late 19th century that a law decreed that the same hereditary surnames were to be passed on from fathers to their children. Formerly, the surnames of most children had been formed by adding -son or -dotter to the father's given name. This meant that succeeding generations in a family had different surnames. Although this is a complicating factor, it is not an insurmountable one for ancestor-tracers.

RECOMMENDED GUIDES:

Cradled in Sweden by Carl Erik-Johansson, Everton Publishers, Logan, Ut., 1972.

Records of Genealogical Value for Sweden, Series D, No. 3, Genealogical Society of Utah, Salt Lake City, Ut.

Church Records of Sweden, Series D, No. 15, General Church Distribution Center, 1999 West 1700 South, Salt Lake City, Ut.

Switzerland

Prior to 1876, the registrations of births, marriages and deaths in Switzerland were the responsibility of the various religious denominations. Since 1876 the registrations have been handled by civil authorities in the twenty-two cantons (states).

In the northern and eastern cantons, German is the predominant language. French is the language in the central and western cantons, and Italian is the language south of the Alps.

When requesting copies of vital statistics' documents, write to the municipal official in the town of your ancestors.
In German-speaking cantons:

> Zivilstandinspectorat
> CH- (Name of town), Switzerland

In French-speaking cantons:

> Officier d'Etat Civil
> CH- (Name of town), Switzerland

In Italian-speaking cantons:

> L-Ufficiale dello Stato Civile
> CH- (Name of town), Switzerland

RECOMMENDED GUIDES:

Handy Guide to Swiss Genealogical Records by Jared Suess, Everton Publishers, Logan, Utah, 1979.

Tracing Your Swiss Roots by Maralyn A. Wellauer, 3239 North 58th St., Milwaukee, Wisconsin.

Major Genealogical Record Sources in Switzerland, Series C, No. 2, Genealogical Society of Utah, Salt Lake City, Utah.

Swiss Genealogical Research by P. A. Nielsen, Donning Co., Virginia Beach, Virginia, 1979.

Important Advice for the Future Authors of This Heritage Book

Writing the Story of Your Family

You are going to be the author of a treasured volume which will be read and enjoyed by the members of your living family and by your descendants in the generations to come. Future generations will use the information you've recorded when they continue to trace the ancestry of your family into the past. So we urge you to resist the natural impulse to make permanent pen-and-ink entries in this book as ideas occur to you.

We cannot overemphasize the importance of first drafting everything you're going to record on separate sheets of paper. Then check and recheck your dates and facts for accuracy: be certain that every word and name is spelled accurately. Make sure that your wording and phraseology are exactly as you want them to be.

After you've followed this simple procedure, you can make your entries in the book with the assurance that the clarity and precision of your writing will be appreciated by your future readers.

We hope that you will write freely about any subjects which you consider appropriate in the various chapters of the Family Biographies and Family Memories sections. At the beginning of each of these chapters we have suggested some ideas which you might like to write about.

Mounting Your Family Pictures

As you turn the pages of this book, you will often see the words "Place Photo Here." Usually they appear in a frame where you can mount a 3-inch by 3³/₄-inch photo. We are not suggesting that these are the only spaces where you should mount pictures.

For instance, you can paste pictures over the full-page, full-color photographs where there is space for a large 8-inch by 10-inch photograph or for as many small pictures as you can fit in neatly. You can also mount pictures as indicated for the recording of vital statistics, family biographies and memories. In each case, be sure to write a caption with the names of the people, the date, place, etc.

There are many other places where you can mount pictures. For example, eight pages have been allocated for the biographies of brothers and sisters. Very possibly, you can use some of these pages for mounting pictures.

When mounting the above materials in this book, do not use a water-base paste which will result in warping and wrinkling. A rubber cement or acetate cement are far more preferable. We suggest that you consult your local photo processor, stationer or librarian for their recommendations as to the best type and brand to use.

Preparing Photos for Mounting

Probably some of your photos are ready for pasting in your Heritage Book in their present form. However, in the case of many photos, you will want to make some adjustments in order to fit the picture into the available space, or to emphasize certain elements on the photo itself.

There are two ways to accomplish this. You can "crop" off unwanted subject matter by cutting off the top, bottom or sides of the picture to suit your own taste. We suggest that you use a single-edged sharp razor and ruler to make a clean cut.

Sometimes you can mount your cropped picture "as is" on its appropriate page. At other times you might want to increase or reduce the size of the picture. Take the photo or the negative to your local photo dealer (preferably a store that specializes in developing and printing) and explain your needs to him. Often they can produce results which are beyond your expectations.

The materials which you mount on pages or store in envelopes need not be limited to photographs and snapshots. As suggested above, you can also preserve many other types of memorabilia here: important family documents, letters, wedding invitations, military records, business cards, newspaper clippings, official records, etc.

Making Storage Envelopes

Extra photos can also be stored in your Heritage Book. Just take a 7½-inch by 10½-inch manila envelope, cut off the top two or three inches and paste the envelope securely to the page. Or, you can cut an envelope in half, seal the bottom ends and mount both halves in the book.

You can also paste storage envelopes on the inside front and inside back cover of the book. Common sense will tell you how many photos or documents you can insert in these envelopes without distorting the book.

Highlighting Your Handwriting

From time to time we've used highly decorative initial letters at the beginning of paragraphs in this Heritage Book.

You too can add an attractive and distinctive touch to your entries by using calligraphic letters to start paragraphs or captions or in any way that appeals to you. Just be sure to practice the calligraphic style before writing in ink on these pages.

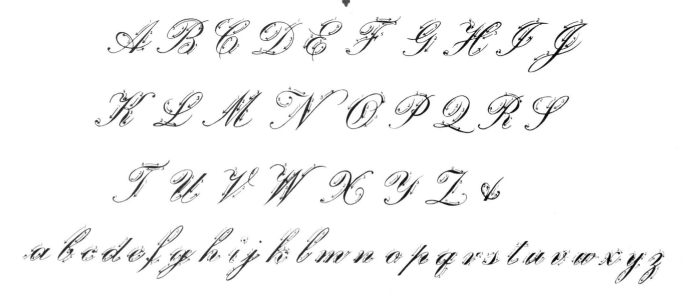